GLOSSARY OF GAꞁ

AND

HORTICULTURAL TERMS

FRENCH-ENGLISH AND ENGLISH-FRENCH

compiled by

ALAN S. LINDSEY

HADLEY PAGER INFO

Third Edition 2004

ISBN 1-872739-14-8

(First Edition 1998   ISBN 1-872739-06-7)
(Second Edition 2001   ISBN 1-872739-10-5)

HADLEY PAGER INFO
Leatherhead, Surrey, England

FOREWORD

The popularity of earlier editions of the Glossary of Gardening and Horticultural Terms among gardeners and market gardeners resident in France has encouraged the author to produce an expanded third edition which now includes nearly two thousand terms together with appended lists of medicinal plants, and of the commoner birds and butterflies found in France. The Glossary substantially covers the majority of garden plants and shrubs, as well as fruit, trees, herbs, vegetables, procedures, equipment, pests, etc. For plants and trees, where possible, the Latin genus name has been included, and for certain varieties the full Latin name has been attached. Although in a few instances the gender of the French name could not be authenticated the plant has been listed for completeness.

In general the Glossary matches up the familiar French and English names of pot and garden flowering plants and shrubs. In some cases where the same French name is used for two different plants the attached Latin names provide distinguishing labels.

The Glossary should prove invaluable to those embarking on gardening or horticultural activities in France or other French speaking regions, as well as to naturalists, translators and exporters.

A.S.L.

Abbreviations Used

adj	adjective	*v*	verb
f	feminine	*pl*	plural noun
m	masculine	*inv*	invariant

FRENCH-ENGLISH

A

abat-vent *m, inv* windbreak
abeille *f* bee; honey bee
abélie *f* [Abelia] abelia
abri *m* de jardin garden shed; tool shed
abricot *m* apricot
abricotier *m* apricot tree
acacia *m* acacia
acacia *m* jaune [Caragana] pea tree; caragana
acaena *f* [Acaena] acaena; New Zealand burr
acanthe *f* [Acanthus] bear's breeches; bear's foot; acanthus
acarien *m* acarid; acaridan; tick; mite
acarien *m* jaune commun common red spider mite (greenhouse)
acarien *m* rouge red spider mite (fruit tree)
ache *f* [Levisticum] wild celery; lovage; smallage; water parsley
achillée *f* millefeuille [Achillea millefolium] achillea; yarrow; milfoil
acidité *f* d'un sol soil acidity
aconit *m* [Aconitum] monkshood; wolfsbane; aconitum
aconit *m* napel [Aconitum napellus] monkshood
acore *m* [Acorus] sweet flag; sweet rush, acorus
actinidia [Actinidia] actinidia
adiante *m* [Adiantum] maidenhair fern; adiantum
adonis *f* [Adonis] adonis; pheasant's eye; ox-eye
aérateur *m* aerator; lawn aerator
agapanthe *m* [Agapanthus] agapanthus; African lily
agathée *f* amelloïde [Agathaea] blue marguerite, agathaea
agathée *f* céleste [Agathaea] blue marguerite
agérate *m*; ageratum *m* [Ageratum] ageratum; floss flower
agrion *m* damselfly; dragonfly
agripaume *f* [Leonurus cardiaca] motherwort

agrostemme *f* en couronne [Agrostemma] rose campion; agrostemma
agrostide *f*; agrostis *m* [Agrostis] agrostis; bent grass; cloud grass
agrume *m* citrus fruit
aiguille *f* de pin pine needle
ail *m* garlic
ail *m* décoratif [Allium] allium; ornamental allium
ajonc *m*; ajonc d'Europe [Ulex europaeus] furse; gorse
akebia [Akebia] akebia
alchémille *f* [Alchemilla] alchemilla; ladies mantle
aleurode *m* whitefly
aleurode *m* des serres whitefly (greenhouse)
alisier *m* blanc [Sorbus aria] whitebeam
alisier *m* torminal [Sorbus torminalis] wild service tree
allée *f* garden path
aloès *m* aloe
alstrœmère *f* [Alstroemeria] Peruvian lily
alysse *f*; alysson *m* [Alyssum] alyssum; madwort
amande *f* almond
amandier *m* [Prunus dulcis] almond tree
amarante *f* à fleurs en queue [Amaranthus] amaranthus; love-lies-bleeding
amaryllis *f* amaryllis
ambroisie *f* ambrosia; wormseed, ragweed
aménagements *mpl* paysagers landscaping
ameublir *v* la terre to loosen or break up the ground; to mellow the soil
amour-en-cage *m* [Physalis alkekengi] Chinese lantern
anagallide *f* [Anagallis] anagallis; pimpernel
ancolie *f* [Aquilegia] aquilegia; columbine
andromède *f* [Andromeda] moor wort; wild rosemary; andromeda
androsace *f* laiteuse [Androsace] rock jasmine; androsace
anémone *f* [Anemone] anemone

anémone *f* pulsatille *[Pulsatilla]* pasque-flower

aneth *m*, aneth odorant; fenouil *m* bâtard;faux-fenouil *[Anethum]* dill

angélique *f*; angélique *f* de Bohême *[Angelica]* angelica

angélique *f* de Chine *[Aralia]* Chinese angelica tree; aralia

anguillule *f* eelworm

annuelle *f* annual (plant)

anthémis *f* *[Anthemis]* rock chamomile; anthemis

anthémis *f* des teinturiers; œil-de-bœuf *m* *[Anthemis]* chamomile

anthure *m* *[Anthurium]* anthurium; flamingo plant

antifourmis *adj* ant destroying; ant killing

antilimaces *fpl* compo; granulés *mpl* antilimaces; slug pellets

antinuisible *m* pesticide

antirrhine *f* *[Antirrhinum]* antirrhinum

aphidés *mpl*; aphidiens *mpl* aphis; aphids; plant-lice; greenfly

aphis *m* aphis; greenfly

appât *m* antilimaces slug bait

aquilegia f; aquilégie *f* *[Aquilegia]* aquilegia; columbine

arabis *f*; arabette *f* *[Arabis]* arabis; wall cress

araignée *f* spider

araignée *f* rouge red spider

araucaria *m* *[Araucaria]* monkey puzzle tree

arbousier *m*; arbousier *m* commun *[Arbutus]* strawberry tree; arbutus

arbre *m* tree

arbre *m* à feuilles caduques deciduous tree

arbre *m* à feuilles persistantes evergreen (tree)

arbre *m* à fraises *[Arbutus]* strawberry tree

arbre *m* à grives *[Sorbus]* rowan tree; mountain ash

arbre *m* à perruque *[Cotinus]* wig sumac; smoke tree; cotinus

arbre *m* aux quarante écus *[Ginkgo biloba]* maidenhair tree; ginkgo

arbre *m* de Judée *[Cercis]* Judas tree

arbre *m* franc de pied ungrafted tree; maiden tree

arbre *m* fruitier fruit tree

arbre *m* vert evergreen

arbrisseau *m* shrub

arbuste *m* shrub; bush

arbuste *m* à fleurs flowering shrub

arbuste *m* d'ornement ornamental shrub

arbuste *m* fruitier fruit shrub

arctotis *[Arctotis]* arctotis

arénaire *f* *[Arenaria]* sand wort; arenaria

argousier *m* *[Hippophae]* sallow-thorn; sea-buckthorn; hippophae

aristoloche *f* *[Aristolochia]* birthwort; aristolochia

armeria *f*; armérie *f*; armeria *f* commune *[Armeria]* armeria; thrift

armoise *f* *[Artemesia]* artemesia; sagebush

arnica *f* des montagnes; arnique *f* des montagnes *[Arnica]* arnica; lamb's skin

arracher *v* to pull up; to pull out (eg weeds)

arracheuse *f* lifter; grubber

arroche *f* *[Atriplex]* orache; atriplex

arrosage *m*; arrosement *m* watering; sprinkling; spraying (lawn etc)

arroser *v* to water; to sprinkle; to spray (lawn etc)

arroseur *m* sprinkler

arroseur *m* oscillant oscillating sprinkler

arroseur *m* rotatif rotating sprinkler

arrosoir *m* watering can

art *m* de faire des bouquets flower arrangement

artichaut *m* *[Cynara scolymus]* globe artichoke

arum *m*; pied-de-veau *m*; gouet *m* d'Italie *[Arum]* cuckoo pint; lords and ladies; wake robin; wild arum

arum *m* maculé *[Arum]* lords and ladies

asaret *m* *[Asarum]* asarum, wild ginger

aspergerie *f*; aspergière *f* asparagus bed

asperges *fpl* asparagus

aspérule *f* odorante *[Asperula]* woodruff; asperula

asphodèle *m* *[Asphodelus]* asphodel

asphodèle *m* **blanc** *[Asphodeline]* king's spear; asphodeline

assolement *m* rotation of crops

aster *m* *[Aster]* aster

aster *m* **d'automne** *[Aster]* Michaelmas daisy

aster *m* **de Chine** *[Callistephus]* Chinese aster; callistephus

aster *m* **des Alpes; aster alpin** *[Aster alpinus]* Alpine aster

aubépine *f* *[Crataegus oxycantha]* hawthorn; whitethorn

aubergine *f* *[Aubergine]* aubergine; eggplant

aubifoin *m* cornflower

aubour *m* wild guelder rose

aubrétie *f*; **aubretia** *f* *[Aubretia]* aubretia; rock cress

aucuba *m* **de Japon** *[Aucuba]* aucuba

aulne *m*, **aune** *m* *[Alnus]* alder

aune *m* **blanc** *[Alnus incana]* grey alder; European alder

auricule *f* *[Primula auricula]* auricula; bear's ear

aurone *f* **femelle** *[Santolina]* lavender cotton

automne *m* autumn

avoine *f* **d'ornement** *[Avena]* animated oat

azalée *f* *[Rhododendron azalea]* azalea

azalée *f* **de Chine** *[Azalea mollis]* Chinese azalea; azalea mollis

azalée *f* **de Japon** *[Azalea japonica]* Japanese azalea; azalea japonica

azote *m* nitrogen

B

bac *m* container

bac *m* **à fleurs** window-box

bac *m* **à plante** tub

baguenaudier *m* *[Colutea]* bladder-senna; colutea

baguette *f* **d'or** *[Cheiranthus]* wallflower

baie *f* berry

baies *fpl* **comestibles** soft fruit

balai *m* broom; besom

balai *m* **à feuilles** lawn rake

balai *m* **à gazon** lawn rake

balai *m* **de cantonnier** roadsweeper's broom

balayeuse *f* **à gazon** lawn sweeper (machine); leaf sweeper for lawns (machine)

balisier *m* *[Canna]* canna; Indian shot

balsamine *f* *[Balsam]* impatiens, garden balsam; yellow balsam

bambou *m* *[Bamboo]* bamboo

bananier *m* **d'ornement** *[Musa]* ornamental banana plant; musa

banc *m* **de jardin** garden seat

barbe-de-bouc *f* *[Aruncus]* salsify; goat's beard; aruncus

barbeau *m* *[Centaurea]* cornflower

baromètre *m* **de pauvre homme** *[Anagallis]* pimpernel; poor man's weather-glass

bartschia des Alpes *[Bartsia alpina]* Alpine bartsia

basilic *m*; **herbe** *f* **royale; oranger** *m* **du savetier** *[Ocimum basilicum]* basil

basse-tige *m*; **arbre** *m* **à basse-tige** bush tree; low bush tree

bassin *m* ornamental lake; pond; pool

bâton *m* **de Jacob;** *[Asphodelus luteus]* yellow asphodel

bâton *m* **royal** *[Asphodeline]* king's spear

bâton *m* **royal** *[Asphodelus luteus]* asphodel

bêchage *m* digging

bêchard *m* double-headed hoe

bêche *f* spade

bêche-tarière *f* post-hole digger

bêcher *v* to dig; to turn over

bégonia *m*; **bégonie** *f* *[Begonia]* begonia

belladone *f* *[Atropa belladonna]* belladonna; deadly nightshade

belle-de-jour *f* *[Ipomaea]* morning glory; ipomea

belle-de-nuit *f* *[Mirabilis]* marvel of Peru; mirabilis

benoîte *f* *[Geum]* avens; geum

berbéris *m* *[Berberis]* berberis

berbéris *m* **commun** *[Berberis]* barberry

berce *f* géante du Caucase *[Heracleum]* cow parsnip; hogweed; heracleum
bergamotier *m* bergamot tree
bermudienne *f* *[Sisyrinchium]* satin flower; sisyrinchium
bétoine *f* *[Betonica]* betony
bétoine *f* des montagnards; bétoine des Vosges *[Arnica montana]* arnica; mountain arnica
bette *f* chard, Swiss chard
betterave *f* beet; beetroot
bidens *m* *[Bidens]* bidens; burr marigold
bigaradier *m* *[Citrus Bigaradia]* Seville orange tree; bitter orange tree
bignone *f*; bignonia *m* *[Bignonia]* trumpet flower; bignonia
binage *m* (du sol) hoeing
biner *v* (le sol) to hoe
binette *f* hoe; draw hoe
binette *f* à pousser push hoe; Dutch hoe
bineuse *f* rotative rotary hoe
binoche *f* two-pronged hoe
binocher *v* to hoe
binot *m* cultivator; light plough; hoe
bisannuel,-elle *adj* biennial
bisannuelle *f* biennial (plant)
blet, blette *adj* overripe
bleuet *m* *[Centaurea]* cornflower; centaurea
bois-joli *m* *[Daphne]* garland flower; daphne
bonsai *m* bonsai
bordé d'arbres *adj* tree-lined
bottes *fpl* en caoutchouc rubber boots
bottes *fpl* PVC PVC boots
bougainvillée *f*; bougainvillier *m* *[Bougainvillea]* bougainvillea
bouillie *f* bordelaise; bouillie *f* cuprique; bouillie *f* cupro-calcique Bordeaux mixture
bouillon-blanc *m* *[Verbascum]* mullein; Aaron's rod; verbascum
boule-d'or *f* *[Trollius]* globe flower
boule-de-neige *f* *[Viburnum]* guelder rose; viburnum
bouleau *m* *[Betula pendula]* silver birch; common birch; European birch
bouleau *m* pubescent *[Betula pubescens]* downy birch

bourgeon *m* bud (of plant, tree)
bourgeonnant *adj* budding (plant)
bourgeonner *v* to bud (plant, tree); to shoot
bourrache *f* *[Borago]* borage
bourse-à-pasteur *f* *[Capsella]* shepherd's purse
bouton *m* bud (of flower)
bouton *m* d'argent *[Anaphalis]* anaphalis
bouton *m* d'or *[Ranunculus]* buttercup; kingcup
bouton *m* d'or des marais *[Caltha]* marsh marigold; caltha
bouton *m* de rose rosebud
bouturage *m* propagation by cuttings
bouturage *m* piping (of carnations)
bouture *f* cutting
bouture *f* de racine root cutting
bouturer *v* to propagate (by cuttings), to pipe (carnations)
branche *f* fleurie, une petite spray of blossom
brande *f* 1 brush (vegetation); 2 heathland
brindille *f* twig
brize *f*, briza *f* *[Briza]* quaking grass; briza
brise-vent *m,inv* windbreak
brocoli *m* broccoli
brouette *f* wheelbarrow
broussaille *f* brushwood; undergrowth
broyeur *m* de végétaux shredder
brugnon *m* nectarine
brugonier *m* nectarine tree
brunelle *f* *[Prunella]* self heal; prunella
brunissure *f* potato blight
bruyère *f* heather; heathland; moorland
bruyère *f* d'été *[Calluna]* summer heather; calluna
bruyère *f* d'hiver *[Erica]* winter heath; erica
buddleia *m* *[Buddleia]* buddleia
bugle *f* *[Ajuga]* bugle
buglosse *f* *[Anchusa]* bugloss; alkanet; anchusa
bugrane *f*, arrête-bœuf *m* *[Ononis]* rest harrow; goat root; cammock
buis *m* *[Buxus]* box; box tree; buxus

buis *m* piquant *[Ruscus]* butcher's broom

buisson *m* ardente *[Pyracantha]* evergreen thorn; fire-thorn; pyracantha

bulbe *m* bulb; corm

bulbe *m* à fleur flower bulb

bulbes *mpl* à naturaliser bulbes for naturalisation

bulbille *f* bulbil; bulblet; small bulb, offset bulb

buplèvre *m* *[Bupleurum]* bupleurum; hare's ear

C

cabaret *m* *[Asarum]* asarabacca

cactus *m*; cactier *m* cactus

caduc, caduque *adj* deciduous

cafard *m* cockroach

caillou *m*; cailloux *mpl* stone; pebble

caisse *f* de fleurs flower box

caissette *f* à semis seed tray

calament *m* *[Calamintha]* calamint

calcaire *m* broyé ground limestone

calcéolaire *f* *[Calceolaria]* slipperwort; slipper flower; calceolaria

calice *m* calyx

calla *f* des marais *[Calla]* bog arum; calla

caltha *m* des marais *[Caltha]* marsh marigold; caltha

camélia *m*; camellia *m* *[Camellia]* camellia

camomille *f* *[Anthemis]* camomile; chamomile; anthemis

campagnol *m* field-vole; meadow mouse

campanule *f* *[Campanula]* campanula; bell-flower, Canterbury bell

campanule *f* à feuilles de pêcher *[Campanula persicifolia]* peach-leaved campanula

campanule *f* (à grosses fleurs) *[Campanula]* giant bell-flower; Canterbury bell

campanule *f* à feuilles rondes *[Campanula]* harebell; bluebell;
campanula

canna *m* *[Canna]* canna; Indian shot

canne *f* de Provence *[Arundo]* great reed; arundo

canneberge *f* cranberry

capillaire *m* *[Adiantum]* maidenhair fern; adiantum

capitule *m* flower head

capside *f* du pommier apple capsid bug

capucine *f* *[Tropaeolium]* nasturtium

capucine *f* de canaris *[Tropaeolum canariensis]* canary creeper

capucine *f* grimpante *[Tropaeolum majus]* climbing nasturtium

capucine *f* naine *[Tropaeolum]* dwarf nasturtium

cardamine *f* des prés *[Cardamine]* cuckoo flower; lady's smock; cardamine

carie *f* dry rot

carie *f* humide wet rot

carline *f*; carline vulgaire *[Carlina]* carline thistle

carotte *f* carrot

carpelle *m* carpel

carpocapse *f* des pommes codling moth

carré *m* square plot of land; patch; flower patch

carthame *m* *[Carthamus]* safflower; carthamus

cassis *m* blackcurrant; blackcurrant bush

cassissier *m* *[Ribes nigrum]* blackcurrant bush

cassolette *f* *[Hesperis]* dame's violet; garden rocket

catalpe *f*; catalpa *m* *[Catalpa]* Indian bean tree; catalpa

céanothe *m*; céanote *m* *[Ceanothus]* ceanothus

cèdre *m* *[Cedrus]* cedar; cedrus

cèdre *m* de Liban *[Cedrus libani]* cedar of Lebanon

céleri *m* celery

céleri *m* vivace *[Levisticum]* wild celery; lovage; smallage; water parsley

céleri-rave *m* celeriac

célosie *f* *[Celosia]* celosia

cenelle *f* haw

centaurée *f* *[Erythraea]* centaury

centaurée *f* bleuet *[Centaurea]* blue

bottle; cornflower

centaurée *f* **musquée** *[Centaurea]* sweet sultan; centaurea

céraiste *m* *[Cerastium]* cerastium; chickweed; mouse-ear chickweed

cerfeuil *m* *[Anthricus]* chervil

cérinthe *m* *[Cerinthe]* honeywort

cerisaie *f* cherry orchard

cerise *f* cherry

cerisier *m* *[Prunus avium]* wild cherry tree; gean

cerisier *m* *[Prunus serotina]* cherry (black) tree

cerisier *m* **à fleurs** *[Prunus]* flowering cherry; prunus

cétoine *f* **dorée** rose chafer; rose beetle

chablis *m* wind break

chalef *m* *[Elæagnus]* oleaster; elæagnus

champignon *m* fungus; mushroom

champignon, le; champignon *m* **du bois** dry rot

chancre *m* canker

chanvre *m* **d'eau** *[Eupatorium]* water agrimony

charançon *m* weevil

chardon *m* thistle

chardon *m* **bleu** *[Echinops]* globe thistle; echinops

charme *m* *[Carpinus betulus]* hornbeam

charmille *f* *[Carpinus]* hornbeam hedgerow

charrue *f* **à soc** ribbing plough, mouldboard plough

châssis *m* **chaud** hot frame; heated frame

châssis *m* **froid** cold frame

châssis *m* **hollandais** Dutch light; Dutch frame

châssis *m* **pour culture forcée** forcing frame

châssis *m* **vitré** glazed frame; glass frame

châtaigne *m* chestnut

châtaignier *m*; **châtaignier** *m* **commun**; **marronnier** *m* *[Castanea sativa]* chestnut tree, Spanish chestnut tree; sweet chestnut tree

chaton *m* catkin

chaudron *m* *[Narcissus, pseudo*

Narcissus] daffodil (wild); Lent lily

chaulage *m* liming

chaux *f* lime (mineral)

chaux *f* **agricole** agricultural lime

chaux *f* **éteinte** slaked lime

chaux *f* **magnésienne** magnesian limestone

chaux *f* **vive** quicklime

chélidoine *f* *[Chelidonium]* greater celandine; chelidonium

chêne *m*; **chêne pedonclé**; **chêne rouvre** [Quercus robur] [Quercus pedunculata] oak; English oak

chêne *m* **à glands sessiles; chêne à fleurs sessiles** *[Quercus petraea]* *[Quercus sessiliflora]* sessile oak

chêne *m* **vert** *[Quercus ilex]* holm oak; holly oak

chenille *f* caterpillar

chétif,-ive *adj* puny; weedy; stunted

cheveux *mpl* **de Venus** *[Adiantum]* maidenhair fern

chèvrefeuille *m* **d'hiver** *[Lonicera fragantissima]* winter honeysuckle

chèvrefeuille *m* **des buissons** *[Lonicera]* fly honeysuckle

chicorée *f* curled endive

chiendent *m* **(officinal)** couch grass; twitch

chimonanthe *[chimonanthus]* Chinese winter sweet; chimonanthus

chlorose *f* chlorosis

chou *m* cabbage

chou *m* **d'hiver** winter cabbage

chou *m* **de Chine** Chinese cabbage

chou *m* **frisé** kale; curly kale

chou *m* **de Milan** Savoy cabbage

chou *m* **pommé vert** green cabbage

chou *m* **pommé blanc** white cabbage

chou *m* **roquette** red cabbage

chou *m* **rouge** red cabbage

chou-fleur *m* *[Brassica]* cauliflower

choux *mpl* **de Bruxelles** Brussels sprouts

chrysalide *f* chrysalis

chrysanthème *m* *[Chrysanthemum]* chrysanthemum

chrysope *f* green lace-wing

ciboule *f* *[Allium]* chive

ciboulette *f*; brelette *f [Allium]* chive
cierge *m* 1 *[Cereus]* cereus, torch thistle;
2 *[Verbascum]* verbascum, mullein;
3 *[Euphorbia]* euphorbia, spurge
cinéraire *f [Cineraria]* cineraria
cinéraire *f* maritime *[Senecio]*
groundsel; ragwort; senecio
cirse *m*; cirsium *m [Cirsium; Cnicus]*
fishbone thistle
cisaille *f* à gazon lawn shears; grass
shears
cisaille *f* à haie hedge shears; hedge
clipper
cisaille *f* de jardin shears; garden
shears
cisailles *fpl* shears; pruning shears
ciste *m*; ciste *m* de Crète *[Cistus]* rock
rose; cistus
citron *m* lemon
citron *m* vert lime
citronnier *m* lemon tree
citrouille *f [Cucurbita]* ornamental
gourd; pumpkin; cucurbita
cive *f* chive
civette *f* chive
clarkie *f*; clarkia *m [Clarkia]* clarkia
clématite *f [Clematis]* clematis
clématite *f* des haies *[Clematis]*
traveller's joy; clematis
cloche *f* cloche
cloche *f* d'Irlande *[Molucella]* molucca
balm; molucella
cloporte *m* woodlouse
cloque *f*; cloque du pêcher blight (fruit
trees); peach leaf curl
clôture *f* fence; fencing
clôture *f* en lattis paling fence
cobée *f*; cobea *m [Cobaea]* Mexican ivy
cochène *m [Sorbus]* mountain ash;
rowan
cochenille *f* scale insect; cochineal
insect
cochenille *f* de la vigne grape mealy
bug
cochenille *f* des serres mealy bug
coccinelle *f* ladybird
cœur-de-Jeannette *m [Dicentra]*
bleeding heart; lyre flower
cœur-de-Marie *m [Dicentra]* bleeding

heart; lyre flower, dicentra
cognassier *m [Cydonia]* quince tree
cognassier *m* à fleurs *[Chaenomeles]*
ornamental quince
coing *m* quince
colchique *m* automnal; colchique *m*
d'automne *[Colchicum]* colchicum;
meadow saffron; autumn crocus
coléus *m*; coliole *f [Coleus]* coleus;
flame nettle
coloquinte *f [Cucurbita]* colocynth; bitter
apple
coloris *m* colour
colza *m* rape
composition *f* florale flower
arrangement
compost *m* compost
composter *v* to compost
concombre *m* cucumber
cône *m* cone
conifères *mpl* conifers
consoude *f [Symphytum]* comfrey;
consound; symphytum
conteneur *m* container (eg plastic pot,
etc)
coquelicot *m [Papaver]* corn poppy,
poppy
coquelourde *f* des jardins *[Lychnis*
coronaria] rose campion; dusty miller;
lychnis
coquelourde *f [Pulsatilla (anemone)]*
pasque-flower; dane-flower; pulsatilla
coqueret *m [Physalis]* Chinese lantern;
winter cherry; ground cherry; physalis
corbeille *f* round flower bed
corbeille *f* d'argent *[Alyssum]* sweet
alison; alyssum
corbeille-de-la-mariée *f [Cerastium*
tomentosum] snow-in-summer
corbeille *f* d'or *[Alyssum]* gold dust;
golden tuft; madwort; rock alyssum
corbeille *f* suspendue hanging basket
cordeau *m* string; line
cordeau *m* de jardinier gardener's line
cordon *m* cordon (tree)
cordon *m* de gazon turf border
coréopsis *m [Coreopsis]* coreopsis;
tickseed
coriandre *f [Coriandrum sativum]*

coriander

cornouiller *m* *[Cornus]* dogwood; Cornelian cherry; cornus

cornouiller *m* **sanguin** *[Cornus]* dogwood tree

corydale *m* *[Corydalis]* corydalis; fumitory

corylopsis *[Corylopsis]* corylopsis

cosmos *m* *[Cosmos]* cosmos

cotonéastre *m* *[Cotoneaster]* cotoneaster

couche *f* 1 seedbed; 2 hotbed (mushroom)

couche *f* **à fumier** open hotbed; manure hotbed

couche *f* **chaude** hotbed

couche *f* **de multiplication** propagation bed

couche *f* **froide** cold frame

couche *f* **tiède** temperate frame

coucou *m* 1 *[Primula veris]* cowslip; 2 *[Primula acaulis]* primrose

coudrier *m* *[Corylus avellana]* hazel tree

coulant *m* runner

couleur *f* colour

couleuvre *f* grass snake

coupe-bordures *m* lawn edger; edge cutter

coupe-herbe *m* **à fil** strimmer

couper *v* to cut

couper *v* **à ras du sol** to cut to ground level

courbet *m* billhook

courge *f* gourd

courge *f* marrow

courge *f* **à la moelle** marrow; vegetable marrow

courge *f* **aubergine** marrow; vegetable marrow

courgette *f* courgette; zuchini

couronne *f* **impériale** *[Fritillaria]* crown imperial

couverture *f* **d'humus** mulch

couvrir (se) *v* **de fleurs** to blossom

crachat *m* **de coucou** cuckoo spit

craie *f* chalk

crépis *m*, **crépide** *f* *[Crepis]* crepis; hawksbeard;

cresson *m* cress

cresson *m* **alénois** garden cress

cresson *m* **de fontaine** water cress

crinodendron *m* *[Elaeocarpaceae]* crinodendron

cristalline *f* *[Mesembryanthemum]* ice plant; mesembryanthemum

croc *m* **à défricher** grubbing hook**croc** *m* **à griffer** four-tined clawing hook

croc *m* **à pommes de terre** potato hoe; Canterbury hoe

croc *m* **à rosiers** three-tined soil levelling hook

croc *m* **à sarcler** weed lifter

crocère *m* **de l'asperge** asparagus beetle

crocère *m* **de l'oignon** onion leaf beetle

crocus *m* *[Crocus]* crocus

cueillette *f* picking (of fruit, vegetables)

cueillette *f* **des fruits** fruit crop; fruit cropping

cueillir *v* to pick (flowers, fruit)

cuivre *m*; **cuivre rouge** copper

cultivar *m* cultivar

cultiver *v* cultivate

culture *f* cultivation; crop growing; cropping

culture *f* **maraîchère** vegetable farming; vegetable growing

culture *f* **commerciale** cash crop; commercial growing

culture *f* **de rapport** cash crop

culture *f* **fruitière** fruit farming

culture *f* **fruitière commerciale** commercial fruit growing

culture *f* **fruitière et maraîchère** fruit and vegetable growing

culture *f* **hâtée** early crop; early cultivation

culture *f* **hydroponique** hydroponics

culture *f* **maraîchère commerciale** commercial vegetable growing

culture *f* **maraîchère sous verre** vegetable growing under glass

culture *f* **retardée** late crop

culture *f* **sans sol** hydroponics

cultures *fpl* **fruitières** fruit crops

cyclamen *m* *[Cyclamen]* cyclamen

cyprès *m* *[Cupressus]* cypress; cupressus

cyprès *m* chauve *[Taxodium]* bald cypress; swamp cypress; taxodium

cyprès *m* de Lawson *[Chamaecyparis lawsonia]* cypress, Lawson

cytise *m* 1 laburnum; 2 broom

cytise *m* des Alpes Alpine laburnum; Scotch laburnum

cytise *m* pluie d'or *[Laburnum vulgare]* laburnum; golden rain tree

D

dahlia *m* *[Dahlia]* dahlia

dahlia *m* pompon *[Dahlia]* pompon dahlia

dalle *f* flagstone; paving stone

damas *m* 1 damson; 2 dame's violet

daphné *m* *[Daphne]* daphne; garland flower

daphné *m* morillon *[Daphne]* spurge-laurel

dard *m* short shoot

datura *m* *[Datura]* thorn apple; datura

débroussailler *v* to clear (undergrowth or brushwood)

débroussailleuse *f* undergrowth strimmer

déchets *mpl* du jardin garden waste; garden refuse

déchets *mpl* végétaux vegetation waste

défeuillaison *f* leaf drop; leaf fall

défleurir *v* to deflower

défoliation *f* leaf fall; leaf drop

défricher *v* to clear land (for cultivation); to bring land into cultivation

delphinium *m* *[Delphinium]* delphinium

demi-tige *m*; arbre *m* en demi-tige half standard

dent-de-chien *f* *[Erythronium]* dog's tooth violet, erythronium

dent-de-lion *f* dandelion

dentaire *f* à neuf feuilles *[Dentaria]* toothwort, coralwort

dentelaire *f* d'Europe *[Plumbago]* leadwort; plumbago

dépérissement *m* withering; decaying

déplantoir *m* garden trowel

déplier *v*; se déplier *v* to unfold; to open out

déraciner *v* to dig up (a plant); to root out; to disroot

désespoir *m* des peintres *[Saxifraga]* London pride

désherbage *m* weeding; weed-killing

désherbant *m* weed-killer; herbicide

désherbant *m* sélectif selective weed-killer

désherber *v* to weed

désherbeuse *f* weeding machine; weeder

desséché *adj* withered, dry

dessécher *v*; se dessécher *v* to wither (plant); to drain (land)

dessinateur, *m* -trice *f* de jardins paysagers landscape gardener

détritus *mpl* de jardin garden rubbish

deutzia *[deutzia]* deutzia

dévidoir *m* hose reel

dianthus *m* *[Dianthus]* dianthus (carnations, pinks, etc)

digitale *f* (pourprée); digitale pourpre *[Digitalis]* foxglove; purple foxglove

dimorphotheca *[Dimorphotheca]* star of the Veldt; Cape marigold; dimorphotheca

diviser *v* to divide; to separate out; to fork (tree trunk)

doradille *f* *[Asplenium]* doradilla; asplenium, spleenwort

dormant *adj* dormant

doronic *m*; doronic *m* du Caucase *[Doronicum]* leopard's bane

doryphore *m* potato beetle; Colarado beetle

Douglas vert; sapin de Douglas *[Pseudotsuga menziesii]* Douglas fir; Oregon pine

douve *f* ditch (open); ditch (between fields)

dracéna *m* *[Dracaena]* dragon (blood) tree

drageon *m* root sucker

drageon *m* sucker

drageonnage *m* propagation by root cuttings

dragonnier *m* *[Dracaena]* dragon tree, dracaena
drainage *m* drainage; draining
drainer *v* to drain
drosère *f*; droséra *f* *[Drosera]* sundew; youthwort, drosera
dryade *f* à huit pétales *[Dryas]* mountain avens

E

ébourgeonnement *m*; ébourgeonnage *m* disbudding
ébourgeonner *v* to disbud
ébranchage *m* pruning; lopping; thinning
ébrancher *v* to prune; to lop
ébrancheur *m* lopping shears; pruner
ébranchoir *m* pruning hook
échalas *m* de vigne stake (for vine)
échalote *f* à maturité shallot
échalote *f* nouvelle spring onion
échelle *f* ladder
échenilloir *m* tree pruner; branch lopper; pole pruner
échenilloir-élagueur *m* tree pruner
écheveria *m* *[Echeveria]* echeveria
écimage *m* topping (off); polling
écimer *v* to top (off); to poll
éclaircir *v* to thin out (seedlings, hedge)
éclaire *f*, grande *[Chelidonium majus]* greater celandine
éclaire *f*, petite*[Ranunculus ficaria]* lesser celandine
écorce *f* bark (of tree)
écorce *f* de pin maritime maritime pine bark
écureil *m* squirrel
écusson *m* shieldbud (for grafting)
écussonnage *m* budding
écussonner *v* to bud (tree)
écussonnoir *m* budding knife
edelweiss *m* (des Alpes) *[Leontopodium]* edelweiss; leontopodium
égaliser *v* to level out (soil)
effeuiller (s') *v* to shed its petals
églantier *m* dog rose bush

églantine *f* dog rose; wild rose
égoïne *f* hand saw (small)
élagage *m* pruning; lopping; thinning
élaguer *v* to prune; to thin out
élagueur *m* pruning hook; pruning shears
ellébore *m* blanc *[Veratrum]* false hellebore; white hellebore
ellébore *m* noire *[Helleborus]* Christmas rose; helleborus
ellébore *m* vert; hellébore vert *[Helleborus viridis]* bear's foot; green hellebore
elsholtzia *m* *[Elsholtzia]* elsholtzia
émettre *v* to send out; to give out (eg shoots)
emiettage *m* crumbling; breaking up (clod); pulverising
émietter *v* to crumble; to break into pieces
émondage *m* pruning, lopping; thinning
émonder *v* to prune; to trim
émondoir *m* pruner; pruning hook
émousser *v* to remove moss from
émousseur *m* moss remover
empoter *v* to pot
encensier *m* rosemary
enclos *m* paddock; enclosure
endive *f* endive; chicory
engrais *m* fertilizer
engrais *m* chimique artificial fertilizer; chemical fertilizer
engrais *m* minéral mineral fertlizer; inorganic fertilizer
enherber *v*; couvrir *v* d'herbe to grass over (land, field)
enrichir *v* to enrich
ensemencement *m* seeding
ente *f* scion; graft
épandeur *m* zspreader
épandeur *m* à engrais fertilizer spreader
épandeur *m* à tracter trailer spreader
épandeur de fumier manure spreader
épanouir (s') *v* to come into bloom ; to come into blosom; to burst into bloom
épandre *v* to spread
éperonnière *f* *[Linaria]* 1 larkspur, 2 toadflax
épervière *f* *[Hieracium]* hawkweed; hieracium

éphémère; éphémère *f* de Virginie
[Tradescantia] spiderwort; tradescantia
épi *m* spike
épi *m* d'eau pondweed; water spike
épiaire *f*; stachyde *f* [Stachys] hedge
nettle; stachys; wound wort
épicéa *m* [Picea] spruce
épicéa *m* commun [Picea abies]
Norway spruce
épillet *m* spikelet; spicule
épilobe *m*; épilobe *m* à épi [Epilobium]
willow herb; epilobium
épimède *f* [Epimedium] barrenwort;
epimedium
épinard *m* spinach
épine *f* thorn
épine *f* blanche [Crataegus] hawthorn
épine *f* noire [Prunus spinosa]
blackthorn; sloe bush
épine-vinette *f* [Berberis] berberis
épineux,-euse *adj* prickly; thorny
époque *f* de plantation planting season;
planting time
érable *m* [Acer] maple
érable *m* champêtre [Acer] common
maple; field maple
érable *m* du Japon [Acer] japanese
maple
érable *m* plane [Acer] Norway maple
érable *m* sycomore [Acer] sycamore;
sycamore maple; great maple
éranthe *m* [Eranthis] winter aconite;
eranthis
érigéron *m* [Erigeron] fleabane;
erigeron
érine *f* des Alpes [Erinus] erinus
érythrone *m* [Erythronium] dog's tooth
violet; erythronium
escabeau *m* stepladder; pair of steps
escargot *m* snail; garden snail
eschscholtzie *f* [Eschscholtzia]
Californian poppy; eschscholtzia
escionner *v* to disbud
escionnnement *m* disbudding
espalier *m* espalier; trellis
esparcette *f* [Onobrychis] sainfoin
essouchage *m* grubbing out stumps;
uprooting
essoucher *v* to grub out stumps

estival *adj* summer; estival
estragon *m* [Artemisia] tarragon
étai *m* stake
étaler *v* to spread out
étamine *f* stamen
étang *m* pond; pool
étayage *m* staking
étayer *v* to stake
été *m* summer
étêter *v* to pollard (a tree)
étoile *f* jaune [Gagea] yellow star of
Bethlehem
être *v* en fleur(s) to blossom
eucalyptus *m* eucalyptus
eulalia *m* [Miscanthus] eulalia
eupatoire *f* à feuilles de chanvre
[Eupatorium] hemp agrimony;
eupatorium
euphorbe *f* [Euphorbia] spurge;
euphorbia
exochorda [Exochorda] exochorda
exposition *f* de fleurs; exposition
florale flower show
extirper *v* to eradicate; to root out; to pull
out (weeds)

F

façon *f* attention; dressing
donner *v* une façon à la terre to till the
land; to give the soil a dressing
faire *v* un croisement de to cross-
fertilize (plants)
faire *v* une recolte to produce a crop
fané *adj* withered
fane *f* haulm (of potatoes etc)
faner *v*; se faner *v* to wilt (flower)
fanes *fpl* de navets turnip tops
fauchage *m* mowing (of hay), cutting;
reaping
faucher *v* to scythe; to mow; to cut
fauchet *m* 1 hay rake; 2 billhook
faucille *f* sickle; hand scythe
faux *f* scythe
faux acacia *m* [Robinia] false acacia
faux bouleau *m* hornbeam

faux conifère *m* *[Kochia]* summer cypress; kochia

faux ébénier *m* laburnum; golden rain tree

faux platane *m* *[Acer pseudoplatanus]* sycamore (maple)

fayard *m* *[Fagus sylvatica]* beech

fenouil *m* fennel

fenouil *m* bâtard dill

fertilisation *f* fertilization; fertilizing

fétuque *f* *[Festuca]* fescue grass

feuillaison *f* foliation

feuille *f* leaf; petal

feuille *f* de chêne oak-leaf lettuce

feuille *f* de rose rose leaf; rose petal

feuille *f* de vigne vine leaf

feuilles *fpl* caduques deciduous leaves

feuilles *fpl* persistantes persistant leaves; evergreen

feuillu,-e *adj* leafy; deciduous; broad-leaved

feuillus (les) *mpl* deciduous trees

fève *f* *[Vicia faba]* broad bean

ficaire *f* *[Ranunculus ficaria]* lesser celandine

figue *f* fig

figuier *m* *[Ficus carica]* fig tree

figuier *m* de Barbarie *[Opuntia]* prickly pear

fil *m* string

filet *m* net; netting (over fruit bushes, etc)

flageolet *m* kidney bean (small)

flèche *f* d'eau *[Sagittaria]* arrow head

flétri *adj* withered

flétrir *v*; se flétrir *v* to wilt (flower); to wither

fleur *f* flower; bloom

fleur *f* coupée cut flower

fleur *f* d'oranger orange blossom

fleur *f* de coucou; coucou *m* *[Narcissus]* daffodil

fleur *f* de la passion *[Passiflora]* passion flower

fleur *f* fanée dead bloom; wilted bloom

fleurir *v* to come into bloom; to bloom (tree); to blossom; to come into blossom; to burst into bloom

fleuriste (m,f); boutique *f* de fleuriste

florist; flower shop

fleurs *fpl* de cerisier cherry blossom

fleur(s), en in bloom, in flower

floraison *f* bloom; blossom; flowering; efflorescence

floral,-e *adj* floral; flower

floralies *fpl* flower show; floral festival

foliation *f* foliation

fongicide *m* fungicide

fongicide *m* systémique systemic fungicide

forçage *m* forcing

forcer *v* to force

forficule *f* earwig

forsythia *m* *[Forsythia]* forsythia

fossé *m* ditch

fougère *f* fern

fougère *f* aspidie *[Polystichum setiferum]* soft shield fern; hedge fern

fougère plume d'autruche *[Matteucia struthiopteris]* ostrich feather fern; shuttlecock fern

fourche *f* à bêcher fork; garden fork, spading fork

fourche *f* à fleurs hand fork

fourche *f* à foin hay fork

fourche-beche *f* garden fork

fourmi *f* ant

fourmilière *f* ant's nest; anthill

fouteau *m* *[Fagus sylvatica]* beech

fragon *m*; fragon *m* épineux *[Ruscus]* butcher's broom

fraise *f* strawberry

fraise *f* des bois wild strawberry

fraise *f* sauvage wild strawberry

fraiseraie *f* strawberry bed

fraisier *m* *[Fragaria]* strawberry plant

fraisière *f* strawberry bed

framboise *f* raspberry

framboisier *m* *[Rubus]* raspberry bush; raspberry cane; rubus

franc *m*; arbre *m* franc cultivar

franc de pied ungrafted; own-rooted

fraxinelle *f* *[Dictamnus]* fraxinella; false dittany; burning bush; dictamnus

freesia *m* *[Freesia]* freesia

frêne *m* *[Fraxinus excelsior]* common ash; European ash

fritillaire *f* *[Frittillaria]* fritillary; fritillaria

fritillaire *f* méléagride; fritillaire *f* **damier** *[Fritillaria]* snake's head; chequered daffodil

fruit *m* **d'églantier** hip

fruits *mpl* **charnus** soft fruit

fruits *mpl* **décidus** windfalls

fruits *mpl* **rouges** soft fruit

fruits *mpl* **tombés** windfalls

fuchsia *m* **de pleine terre** *[Fuchsia]* fuchsia

fuchsia *m* **du Cap** *[Phygelius]* Cape fuchsia

fumier *m* manure

fumier *m* **de cheval** horse manure

fumigation *f* fumigation

fumiger *v* to fumigate

fumure *f* manure; manuring

funkie *f* *[Funkia]* plantain-lily; funkia

fusain *m* *[Euonymus]* spindle-tree; euonymus

fût *m* bole (of tree)

G

gaillarde *f* *[Gaillardia]* gaillardia; blanket flower

galéga *m* *[Galega]* goat's rue, galega

gardénia *m*; **gardénie** *f* *[Gardenia]* gardenia

gâté *adj* rotten (fruit)

gaulthérie *f* *[Gaultheria]* gaultheria

gaura *[Gaura]* gaura

gazania *[Gazania]* treasure flower

gazon *m* lawn, turf

gazon *m* **d'Espagne** *[Armeria]* armeria; thrift

gazonner *v* to grass over (garden)

genêt *m* *[Genista]* broom

genêt *m* **d'Espagne** *[Genista]* Spanish broom; genista

genévrier *m* *[Juniperus]* juniper

gentiane *f* *[Gentiana]* gentian

gentiane *f* **de printemps; gentiane printanière** *[Gentiana]* blue gentian

gentiane *f* **des marais** *[Gentiana]* autumn bells; windflower

géranium *m* *[Pelargonium]* geranium; cranesbill; pelargonium

géranium des fleuristes; géranium des jardins *[Pelargonium]* geranium; pelargonium

géranium *m* **lierre** *[Pelargonium]* ivy geranium; ivy-leaved geranium, pelargonium

gerbéra *[Gerbera]* barbeton daisy

germandrée *f* *[Teucrium]* germander; teucrium

germoir *m* seed box; seed tray

gesse *f* [Lathyrus] vetch; everlasting pea

gesse *f* **odorante** *[Lathyrus odoratus]* sweet pea

giroflée *f* **des jardins** *[Matthiola]* stock

giroflée *f* **jaune; giroflée** *f* **des murailles** *[Cheiranthus]* wallflower; cheiranthus

giroflée *f* **quarantaine** *[Matthiola]* ten-week stock

glaïeul *m* *[Gladiolus]* gladiolus; corn flag; sword grass; sword lily

glaise *f* clay

gloire *f* **de neige** *[Chionodoxa]* glory-of-the-snow, chionodoxa

gloxinie *f* *[Gloxinia]* gloxinia

glycérie *f* *[Glyceria]* sweet grass; glyceria

glycine *f* *[Wistaria]* wisteria; wistaria

glycine *f* **de Chine** *[Wistaria]* wistaria

glycine *f* **de Japon** *[Wistaria]* wistaria

gobelets *mpl* *[Omphalodes]* navelwort; pennywort

godet *m* **de plastique** plastic pot/container/holder (for plant)

godétia *f*; **godétie** *f* *[Godetia]* godetia

gombo *m* okra; gombo; ladies fingers

gouet *m* **d'Italie** *[Arum]* arum; lords and ladies

gourmand *m* sucker

gourde *f* gourd

gousse *f* **d'ail** clove of garlic

gousse *f* **de pois** pea pod

goutte-de-sang *f* *[Adonis]* pheasant's eye; adonis

graine *f* seed

graine *f* **de moutarde** mustard seed

graineterie *f* seed merchant (shop)

grainetier *m*; **grainetière** *f* seed

merchant (person)

graminées *fpl* grasses

grande giroflée *f* *[Matthiola]* stock

grassette *f* *[Pinguicula]* bog violet;
butterwort

gratteron *m* *[Galium]* goose grass;
catchweed; cleavers

gratte-cul *m* rosehip

greffage *m* grafting

greffage *m* **à l'anglaise compliqué**
tongue grafting

greffage *m* **à l'anglaise simple** splice
grafting; whip grafting

greffage *m*, **double** double grafting;
intergrafting

greffage en couronne crown grafting;
bark grafting

greffage *m* **en écusson** budding

greffage *m* **en fente** cleft grafting; wedge
grafting

greffage *m* **en incrustation** notch
grafting

greffage *m* **en placage** plate grafting

greffage *m* **sur racine** root grafting

greffe *f* graft; scion

greffe *f* **en couronne** crown graft

greffe *f* **en écusson** budding; shield graft

greffe *f* **en fente** cleft graft

greffer *v* to graft (tree)

greffer *v* **sur franc** to graft onto a cultivar

greffoir *m* grafting knife

greffon *m* graft; scion

grenadier *m* *[Punica]* pomegranate tree;
punica

grenouillette *m* *[Ranunculus]* water
crowfoot

griffe *f* tendril

griffe *f* cultivator; claw rake

griffe *f* **à fleurs** small hand cultivator

griffe *f* **trois dents** three-pronged
cultivator

griffe-bineuse *f* claw cultivator

griffer *v* to claw; to rake (soil); to scratch
(brambles)

grillage *m* wire netting; wire mesh

grimpant *adj* climbing

gros-pied *m* clubroot (of cabbage)

groseille *f* **à grappes** *[Ribes]* currant
(red, white)

groseille *f* **à maquereau** *[Ribes]*
gooseberry

groseille *f* **noire** blackcurrant

groseille *f* **verte** gooseberry

groseillier *m* currant bush

groseillier *m* **à fleurs** *[Ribes]* flowering
currant; ribes

groseillier *m* **à grappes** *[Ribes [rubrum]]*
red currant; white currant bush

groseillier *m* **à maquereau** gooseberry
bush

groseillier *m* **noir** blackcurrant bush

guêpe *f* wasp

guêpier *m* wasp's nest

gueule-de-loup *f* *[Antirrhinum]*
antirrhinum; snapdragon

gui *m* *[Viscum]* mistletoe; viscum

gunnère *f* *[Gunnera]* prickly rhubarb;
gunnera

gypsophile *f* *[Gypsophila]* gypsophila,
chalk plant; gauze flower

H

habiller *v* to trim (roots)

hache *f* axe

hachette *f* hatchet

haie *f* hedge; hedgerow

hamamélis *m* *[Hamamelis]* hamamelis;
witch-hazel

hangar *m* shed; lean-to; outhouse;
warehouse

hangar à recoltes Dutch barn; open-
sided barn

hanneton *m* cockchafer; maybug

haricot *m* haricot bean; kidney bean

haricot *m* **à filets** runner bean

haricot *m* **à rames** runner bean

haricot *m* **d'Espagne** scarlet runner

haricot *m* **vert** French bean

hâter *v* to force

hâtiveau *m* early fruit; early vegetable

haute-tige *m*; **arbre** *m* **en haute-tige**
standard (tree)

hélianthe *m*; **helianthus** *m* *[Helianthus]*
sunflower; helianthus;

hélianthe *m* **tubéreux** *[Helianthus tuberosus]* Jerusalem artichoke

hélianthème *m*; **helianthemum** *m* *[Helianthemum]* rock rose; sun rose; helianthemum

héliotrope *m* *[Heliotropium]* heliotrope

héliotrope *m* **du Perou** *[Heliotropium]* heliotrope; cherry-pie

hellébore *m* **d'hiver** *[Eranthis hyemalis]* winter aconite

helléborine *f* *[Serapias]* tongue-flowered orchid; helleborine

hellébore *m*; **ellébore** *m* **noir** *[Helleborus]* christmas rose; hellebore; helleborus

hémérocalle *f*; **hémérocallis** *m* *[Hemerocallis]* day lily; hemerocallis

herbacé *adj* herbaceous

herbe *f* grass; herb

herbe *f* **à foulon** *[Saponaria]* soapwort; saponaria

herbe-à-jaunir *f* *[Genista tinctoria]* dyer's greenweed; woodwaxen; woadwaxen

herbe-à-jaunir *f* *[Reseda luteola]* dyer's rocket; weld; yellowweed

herbe *f* **à mille florins** *[Erythraea]* common centaury; erythraea

herbe *f* **au lait** *[Polygala]* milkwort

herbe *f* **aux anges** *[Angelica]* angelica

herbe *f* **aux turquoises** *[Ophiopogon]* snake's beard; ophiopogon

herbe *f* **aux vipères** *[Echium]* viper's bugloss; echium

herbe *f* **de saint-Jacques** ragwort

herbe *f* **des pampas** *[Cortaderia]* pampas grass; cortaderia

herbe *f* **royale** *[Ocinum basilicum]* basil

herbe *f* **sacrée** *[Salvia officinalis]* sage

herbe-aux-perruches *f* *[Asclepias]* swallow wort; milkweed; asclepias

herbes *fpl* **médicinales** medicinal herbs

herbes *fpl* **potagères** pot herbs

herbicide *adj & m* herbicidal *adj*; herbicide; weedkiller

hérissé,-e *adj* prickly

hérisson *m* hedgehog

hernie *f* **du chou** clubroot (cabbage)

herse *f* harrow

hêtre *m* (**commun**) *[Fagus sylvatica]* beech

heuchère *f* *[Heuchera]* alum root; heuchera

hibiscus *m* *[Hibiscus]* hibiscus

hickory *m* *[Carya]* hickory

hiver *m* winter

hivernage *m* **sous abri** wintering (eg of plants under cover); winter season

hivernal *adj* winter

hormones *fpl* **de bouturage** hormone rooting powder

hortensia *m* *[Hydrangea]* hydrangea

horticulteur *m* market gardener; horticulturist

horticulture *f* horticulture; gardening

horticulture *f* **commerciale** commercial horticulture

houblon *m* *[Humulus]* hop; humulus

houblon *m* **de Japon** hop (Japanese)

houe *f* hoe

houement *m* hoeing

houer *v* to hoe

houette *f* small hoe

houstonia *f* *[Houstonia]* houstonia

houx *m* **commun** *[Ilex aquifolium]* holly; ilex

hoyau *m* mattock

humus *m* humus

hybride *adj & m* hybrid

I

ibéride *f*, **ibéris** *m* *[Iberis]* iberis; candytuft

if *m* *[Taxus]* yew; yew tree; taxus

immortelles *fpl* *[Helichrysum]* everlasting flowers; helichrysum

impatiens *f* *[Impatiens]* impatiens; balsamine; Zanzibar balsam; busy Lizzie

impatiente *f* **glanduleuse** *[Impatiens glandulifera]* impatiens

incarvillée *f* *[Incarvillea]* incarvillea

indigotier *m*; **indigofera** *m* *[Indigofera]* indigo plant; indigofera

inerme *adj* thornless

insectes *mpl* **nuisibles** pests
insecticide *m* **polyvalent** universal insecticide
inule *f*; **inula** *f* *[Inula]* inula; fleabane; elecampane
ipomée *f* *[Ipomoea]* morning glory; ipomoea
ipomée *f* **bonne-nuit** *[Ipomoea]* moon-flower
irésine *[Iresine]* iresine
iris *m* **(des marais)** *[Iris]* flag iris
iris *m* **de Sibérie** *[Iris]* Siberian iris
iris *m* **des jardins** *[Iris germanica]* iris; garden iris; German iris
iris *m* **jaune des marais** *[Iris]* yellow iris
iris *m* **nain** *[Iris pumila]* dwarf iris
irrigation *f* irrigation
irriguer *v* to irrigate

JK

jacaranda *m* *[Jacaranda]* jacaranda
jacinthe *f* *[Hyacinthus]* hyacinth
jacinthe *f* **d'eau** *[Eichornia]* water hyacinth
jacinthe *f* **des bois; jacinthe** *f* **sauvage** *[Hyacinthus]* wild hyacinth, bluebell
jacobée *f* *[Senecio jacobaea]* ragwort
jalousie *f* **des jardins** *[Lychnis]* rose campion
jardin *m* garden
jardin *m* **alpin** rock garden
jardin *m* **d'agrément** flower garden, ornamental garden
jardin *m* **d'herbes aromatiques** herb garden
jardin *m* **d'hiver** winter garden; conservatory
jardin *m* **de rapport** market garden; household garden
jardin *m* **de rocaille** rock garden, rockery
jardin *m* **fruitier** orchard
jardin *m* **potager; potager** *m* kitchen garden, vegetable garden
jardin *m* **public** park; public gardens
jardinage *m* gardening

jardiner *v*; **faire** *v* **du jardinage** to garden; to do gardening
jardinier-fleuriste *m* flower grower
jardinier *m* **maraîcher** market gardener; vegetable grower
jardinier *m* **-ière** *f* **paysagiste** landscape gardener
jardinière *f* flower stand; window box, jardinière
jasmin *m* *[Jasminum]* jasmine
jasmin *m* **d'hiver** *[Jasminum]* winter jasmine
jasmin *m* **de Chili** *[Mandevilla]* mandevilla; Chile jasmine
jasmin *m* **de Madagascar** *[Stephanotis floribunda]* stephanotis; Madagascar jasmine
jasmin *m* **de Virginie** *[Tecoma]* trumpet creeper; trumpet flower; tecoma
jasmin *m* **du Cap** Cape jasmin
jasmin *m* **trompette** *[Tecoma]* trumpet creeper; trumpet flower
jaunir *v* to yellow; to turn yellow
jeannette *f* **blanche** *[Narcissus]* pheasant's eye; poet's narcissus
jeannette *f* **jaune** *[Narcissus]* daffodil
jonc *m* *[Juncus]* rush
jonc *m* **fleuri** *[Butomus]* flowering rush; butomus
jonquille *f* *[Narcissus]* daffodil; jonquil
joubarbe *f* *[Sempervivum]* houseleek; Jupiter's beard; sempervivum
julienne *f* **des dames** *[Hesperis]* dame's violet; sweet rocket, hesperis
kalmie *f* *[Kalmia]* kalmia; mountain laurel
kerria *m*; **kerrie** *f* *[Kerria]* kerria; Japanese rose; Jew's mallow, kerria

L

labelle *m* *[Cypripedium]* lady's slipper orchid; cypripedium
labourage *m* 1 tilling; ploughing; 2 arable land
laîche *f* *[Carex]* sedge; carex
laitue *f* lettuce

laitue *f* d'été summer lettuce
laitue *f* pommée cabbage lettuce
lambourde *f* short shoot
lamier *m* tacheté *[Lamium]* dead-nettle;
  archangel
lamier 'White Nancy' *m* *[Lamium
  maculatum]* dead nettle; White Nancy
langue-de-cerf *f* *[Phyllitis]* hart's tongue
  fern; phyllitis
lantana *m*; lantanier *m* *[Lantana]*
  lantana
lapin *m* rabbit
larve *f* larva
larve *f* de la tipule leatherjacket
larve *f* de taupin wireworm
larve *f* du hanneton cockchafer larva;
  cockchafer grub
laurier-cerise *m* *[Prunus]* cherry laurel;
  common laurel, prunus
laurier *m* commun; laurier noble;
  laurier d'Apollon; laurier-sauce *m*
  [Laurus nobilis] noble laurel; bay laurel;
  sweet bay
laurier *m* d'Alexandrie *[Danae]*
  Alexandrian laurel; danae
laurier *m* de Saint-Antoine *[Epilobium]*
  willow herb, epilobium
laurier *m* du Portugal *[Prunus]* Portugal
  laurel
laurier-rose *m*; rose-laurier *m* *[Nerium]*
  oleander; rose laurel; rose bay; nerium
laurier-sauce *m*; laurier d'Apollon
  [Laurus] bay laurel
lavande *f* *[Lavandula]* lavender;
  lavandula
lavatère *f* *[Lavatera]* mallow
lavatère *f* en arbre *[Lavatera]* tree
  mallow; lavatera
lavatère *f* maritime *[Lavatera]* mallow;
  lavatera
légume *m* vegetable
lézard *m* lizard
liatride *f* *[Liatris]* blazing star; Kansas
  feather; liatris
libellule *f* dragonfly
lichen *m* lichen
lierre *m* *[Hedera]* ivy
lierre *m* de canaris *[Hedera canariensis]*
  Canary Island ivy

lierre *m* terrestre *[Glechoma hederacea]*
  rampant ivy; ground ivy
lièvre *m* hare
ligulaire *f*; ligularia *m* *[Ligularia]* leopard
  plant; ligularia
lilas *m* *[Syringa]* lilac (bush, flower),
  syringa
lilas *m* de Chine *[Buddleia]* buddleia
limace *f* du sol; limaces *fpl* slug; slugs
lime *f* lime (citrus)
limettier *m* *[Citrus limetta]* lime tree,
  sweet lime tree (citrus)
limoneux, -euse *adj* alluvial; mud
lin *m* *[Linum]* flax; linum
lin *m* d'Autriche *[Linum]* Austrian flax
linaigrette *f*; jonc *m* à coton
  [Eriophorum] cotton grass; eriophorum
linaire *f*; linaire commune *[Linaria]*
  toadflax; linaria
lis *m*; lys *m* *[Lilium]* lily
lis *m* blanc *[Lilium]* white lily; Madonna
  lily
lis *m* de Japon *[Nerine sarniensis]*
  Guernsey lily; nerine
lis *m* de Saint-Jacques *[Amaryllis]*
  amaryllis belladonna; belladonna lily
lis *m* des étangs *[Nymphaea]* water lily
lis *m* des vallées; lis *m* de mai
  [Convallaria] lily of the valley;
  convallaria
lis *m* du Mexique Mexican lily
lis *m* jaune yellow pond-lily
lis *m* orangé *[Lilium]* orange lily; tiger lily
lis *m* tigré *[Lilium]* tiger lily
liseron *m*; liset *m*; liseron des champs
  [Convolvulus] convolvulus; bindweed
liseron *m* des haies *[Calystegia]*
  bearbind; bindweed
livèche *f* Levisticum wild celery; lovage;
  smallage; water parsley
lobélie *f* *[Lobelia]* lobelia
loganberry *m* loganberry
lombric *m* earthworm
lotus *m* *[Nelumbium]* Egyptian lotus;
  sacred bean; water bean; nelumbium
louchet *m* peat spade; draining spade
lunaire *f* *[Lunaria]* honesty; satin flower;
  moonwort; lunaria
lupin *m* *[Lupinus]* lupin

lupin *m* vivace *[Lupinus]* perennial lupin
luzule *f* des champs *[Luzula]* sweet
bent
lychnide *f* diurne *[Lychnis]* red campion
lychnide *f*; lychnis *m* *[Lychnis]* rose
campion; lychnis
lysimachie *f*; lysimaque *f* *[Lysimachia]*
loosestrife; yellow pimpernel;

M

magnésium *m* magnesium
magnolia *m*; magnolier *m* *[Magnolia]*
magnolia; magnolia tree
mahonia *m* 'Charity' *[Mahonia x
'Charity']* mahonia 'Charity'
main *f* vert green fingers
maïs *m* maize; sweet corn
maladie *f* des pommes de terre potato
blight
maladie *f* des taches noires; marsonia *f*
black spot disease (roses)
mandarinier *m* mandarin tree
maniveau *m* punnet
manutention *f* de terre working the
ground
marécageux,-euse *adj* boggy; marshy
maraîchage *m* vegetable growing
maraîcher *m* vegetable grower
marcottage *m* layering
marcotte *f* layer; runner
marcotter *v* to layer
marguerite *f* d'automne *[Aster]*
Michaelmas daisy
marguerite *f* dorée *[Chrysanthemum
segetum]* corn marigold; yellow
marigold; yellow chrysanthemum, yellow
ox-eye
marguerite *f* de la Saint-Michel *[Aster]*
Michaelmas daisy
marguerite *f*, grande *[Chrysanthemum]*
marguerite; ox-eye daisy
marguerite *f*, petite *[Bellis]* daisy (lawn)
marjolaine *f* *[Origanum majorana]*
marjoram; sweet marjoram
marron *m* chestnut

marronnier *m* *[Aesculus]* chestnut;
horse chestnut tree
marronnier *m* d'Inde *[Aesculus
hippocastanum]* horse chestnut tree
massette *f* *[Typha]* bulrush; reed mace;
cat's-tail
massif *m* de fleurs clump of flowers
massif *m* de rosiers rosebed
mastic *m* à greffer grafting wax; tree
grafting wax
matricaire *f* feverfew
matricaire *f* camomille wild camomile
matthiole *f*; mathiole *f* *[Matthiola]*
matthiola; ten-week stock
mauvaises herbes *fpl* weeds
mauve *f* *[Malva]* mallow; malva
mélèze *m* *[Larix decidua]* common larch;
European larch
mélilot *[Melilotus]* melilot
mélinet *m* *[Cerinthe]* honeywort; cerinthe
melisse *f* citronnelle *[Melissa]* lemon
balm; melissa
mélisse *f* officinale *[Melittis]* melissa;
balm
mélitte *f*; mélisse *f* sauvage *[Melittis]*
melittis
menthe *f* *[Mentha]* mint
merisier; merisier *m* des oiseaux
[Prunus avium] gean; wild cherry;
mazzard; bird cherry
mérule *m* *[Merulius lacrymans]* dry rot
fungus; merulius
mésembryanthéme *m* *[Mesembry-
anthemum]* mesembryanthemum
méthonique *f* *[Gloriosa]* glory lily;
gloriosa
mettre *v* en jauge to box; to heel in (eg
seedlings)
mignardise *f*; oeillet *f* mignardise
[Dianthus plumarius] pink; garden pink
mignonnette *f* *[Reseda]* mignonette;
reseda
mildiou *m* mildew; brown rot; potato
blight
mildiousé,-e *adj* mildewed; mildewy
mille-pattes *m, inv*; mille-pieds *m, inv*
millipede, centipede
millepertuis *m*; herbe-à-mille-trous
[Hypericum (perforatum)] St. John's

Wort; Aaron's beard; rose of Sharon; tutsan

millepertuis *m* **velu** *[Hypericum]* Aaron's beard

millet *m* millet

mimosa *m* *[Mimosa]* mimosa

mimule *m* *[Mimulus]* mimulus; monkey flower

miscanthe *m* *[Miscanthus]* eulalia

moisissure *f* mould

molène *f* *[Verbascum]* mullein; verbascum

momordique *f* *[Momordica]* momordica

momordique *f* **balsamique** *[Momordica balsamina]* balsam apple

monarde *f* *[Monarda]* horse mint; monarda

monnaie-du-pape *f* *[Lunaria]* honesty; satin flower, lunaria

montbrétia *f*; **montbrétie** *f* *[Crocosmia; Crocosma]* montbretia; crocosmia

monter *v*; **monter en graine** to bolt; to go to seed

motoculteur *m* power driven cultivator

motte *f* **(de terre)** clod (of earth)

motte *f* **adhérant aux racines** rootball

motte *f* **de gazon** turf (single)

mouche *f* **à scie** sawfly

mouche *f* **blanc des serres** whitefly (greenhouse)

mouche *f* **de la carotte** *[Psila rosae]* carrot fly

mouron *m* **rouge; mouron** *m* **des champs** *[Anagallis]* scarlet pimpernel

mousse *f* moss

moutarde *f* **blanche** mustard

moutarde *f* **blanche et cresson** *m* **alénois** mustard and cress

moutarde *f* **des Capucins** *[Cochlearia armoracia]* horseradish

muflier *m* *[Antirrhinum]* antirrhinum

muguet *m* *[Convallaria]* lily of the valley; convallaria

mulot *m* field mouse

multiplication *f* **des plantes** plant propagation

mûr,e *adj* ripe

mûre *f* blackberry; mulberry

mûrier *m* mulberry tree

mûrier *m* **sauvage** blackberry bush, bramble

muscari *m* *[Muscari]* grape hyacinth; muscari

myosotis *m* *[Myosotis sylvatica]* myosotis; forget- me-not; scorpion grass

myosotis *m* **des marais** *[Myosotis]* forget-me-not; myosotis

myriapode *m* myriapod

myrobolan *m* *[Prunus]* cherry plum

myrte *m* *[Myrtus]* myrtle

myrte *m* **des marais** *[Myrica gale]* sweet gale; bog myrtle; Dutch myrtle

myrte *m* **épineux** *[Ruscus]* butcher's broom

myrtille *f* bilberry; blueberry; whortleberry

myrtillier *m* *[Vaccinium myrtillus]* whortleberry bush; bilberry bush

N

nain,-e *adj* dwarf

nandina *[Nandina]* nandina

narcisse *m* *[Narcissus]* narcissus

narcisse *m* **des poètes** *[Narcissus]* poets' narcissus, pheasant's eye

narcisse *f* **sauvage** *[Narcissus]* daffodil

navet *m* turnip

néflier *m* *[Mespilus germanica]* medlar; mespilus

ne m'oubliez pas *m inv* *[Myosotis]* forget-me-not, myosotis

ne-me-touchez-pas *m* *[Impatiens noli-me-tangere]* yellow balsam; touch-me-not

nectarine *f* nectarine

néflier *m* *[Mespilus]* medlar; mespilus

némésia *m* *[Nemesia]* nemesia

nématode *m* eelworm; nematode

nénuphar *m* *[Nuphar]* nenuphar; water-lily

nénuphar *m* **jaune; nénuphar des étangs** *[Nuphar lutea]* yellow water lily; spatter dock

népenthe *m*; **népenthés** *m* *[Nepenthes]* nepenthes; pitcher plant

nepeta *f* *[Nepeta]* catmint; nepeta
nerprun *m* *[Rhamnus]* buckthorn;
rhamnus
nettoyage *m* des souches pruning to
ground level
nettoyer *v* to clean; to clear
nierembergia *[Nierembergia]*
nierembergia
nigelle *f* de Damas *[Nigella]* love-in-a-
mist; nigella
nivéole *f* *[Leucojum]* snowflakes;
leucojum
nodule *m* nodule
noisetier *m* *[Corylus avellana]* hazel
tree; corylus; cobnut (tree); filbert
noisetier *m* de sorcière *[Hamamelis]*
witch-hazel
noisette *f* hazelnut
noix *f* walnut
noix *f*; noyer *m* commun *[Juglans regia]*
walnut tree
nombril *m* de Venus *[Omphalodes]*
navelwort; pennywort; omphalodes
noyer *m* d'Amérique hickory
noyer *m* d'Europe European walnut
noyer *m* noir *[Juglans nigra]* black walnut
nymphéa *m* *[Nymphaea]* water lily;
nymphaea
nymphéa *m* blanc *[Nymphaea]* white
water lily
nymphéa *m* de Zanzibar *[Nymphaea]*
Zanzibar water lily

O

œil *m* bud (of plant, tree)
œil-de-bœuf *m* *[Chrysanthemum]* white
oxeye; oxeye daisy
œil *m* de faisan *[Narcissus]* pheasant's
eye; poet's narcissus
œil-de-paon *m* *[Tigridia]* tiger iris; tigridia
œillet *m* *[Dianthus]* carnation, pink
œillet *m* barbu *[Dianthus]* sweet
William, dianthus
œillet *m* d'Inde *[Tagetes]* French
marigold; African marigold; tagetes

œillet *m* d'Inde, petit *[Tagetes]* French
marigold; tagetes
œillet *m* de chine *[Dianthus]* Chinese
pink
œillet *m* de Pâques *[Narcissus]* poet's
narcissus
œillet *m* de poète *[Dianthus]* sweet
william; dianthus
œnothère *m* *[Oenothera]* oenothera;
evening primrose, godetia
oïdium *m* oidium; vine mildew; powdery
mildew
oignon *m* 1 onion; 2 bulb
oignon *m* d'Espagne Spanish onion
oignon *m*, petit pickling onion
oléastre *m* *[Elaeagnus]* oleaster
oléicole *adj* olive-growing (land); olive ....
oléiculture *f* olive-growing
olive *f* olive
olivette *f*; olivaie *f*; oliveraie *f* olive
grove
olivier *m* *[Olea]* olive tree
ombilic *m* *[Omphalodes]* navelwort,
omphalodes
onagraire *f* *[Oenothera]* evening
primrose
onagre *f* *[Oenothera]* evening primrose
oponce *m* *[Opuntia]* prickly pear
orange *f* amère bitter orange; Seville
orange
oranger *m* *[Citrus]* orange tree
oranger *m* amère *[Citrus]* bitter orange
tree; Seville orange tree
oranger *m* du Mexique *[Choisya]*
Mexican orange; choisya
oranger *m* du savetier *[Ocinum*
basilicum] basil
orchidée *f* *[Orchid]* orchid
orchis *m* wild orchid
orchis *m* militaire military orchid; soldier
orchid
orchis *m* pourpre purple orchid
orchis *m* tacheté *[Orchis maculata]*
spotted orchid
oreille *f* d'ours *[Primula auricula]* bear's
ear
oreille-de-lièvre *f* *[Bupleurum]* hare's ear
oreille-de-souris *f* 1 *[Myosotis sylvatica]*
forget-me-not; myosotis; 2 *[Cerastium]*

mouse-ear chickweed

origan *m* *[Origanum vulgare]* wild marjoram; origano

orme *m* **blanc** *[Ulmus glabra]* wych elm; Scotch elm

orme *m* **d'angleterre; orme champêtre** *[Ulmus campestris] [Ulmus procera]* English elm

orme *m* **de montagne** *[Ulmus glabra]* wych elm; Scotch elm

orme *m*, **hollandais** *[Ulmus x hollandica]* Dutch elm

ormeau *m* elm (young)

ornithogale *m* **à ombelle** *[Ornithogalum]* star of Bethlehem

orpin *m* *[Sedum]* stonecrop; sedum

ortie *f* *[Urtica]* nettle

ortie *f* **brûlante; ortie** *f* **romaine** *[Urtica]* stinging nettle

oseille *f* *[Rumex]* dock; sorrel

osier *m* **fleuri** *[Epilobium]* willow herb; epilobium

osmanthus *m* *[Osmanthus]* osmanthus

osmonde *f* **royale** *[Osmunda]* royal fern; osmunda

outillage *m* equipment; tools

outils *mpl* **de jardinage** garden(ing) tools

oxalide *f* *[Oxalis]* wood sorrel; cape shamrock, oxalis

oxalide *f* **blanche** *[Oxalis]* wood sorrel, oxalis

PQ

pachysandra *[Pachysandra]* pachysandra

paillage *m* mulching

paillasson *m* straw mat

paille *f* srtraw

pailler *v* to mulch

paillis *m* mulch

paillis *m* **annuel** annual mulch

pain *m* **de coucou** *[Oxalis]* wood sorrel; oxalis

palissage *m* training by nailing up trailing plants etc

palmette *f* palmette; fan-trained tree

palmier *m* palm tree

pamplemousse *m* *[Citrus grandis]* grapefruit

panaché *adj* variegated

panais *m* parsnip

pancalier *m* Savoy cabbage

panic *m* **effilé** *[Panicum]* hair grass; panicum

panicaut *m*; **panicaut** *m* **maritime** *[Eryngium]* sea holly; eryngium

panier *m* basket; hand basket

pâquerette *f* *[Bellis]* daisy; oxeye daisy; marguerite

parasite *m* parasite

parasol (en) umbellate; weeping; hanging

parc *m* **floral** flower garden

parfum *m* scent; fragrance

parfumé,-e *adj* scented; perfumed

parisette *f* **à quatre feuilles** *[Paris quadrifolia]* herb Paris; true love (herb)

parmentière *f* potato

parterre *m* flower bed

parterre *m* **de gazon** lawn; grass plot

passe-rose *f* *[Althaea rosea]* hollyhock; rose mallow

passiflore *f* *[Passiflora]* passion flower; passiflora

patate *f* sweet potato, Spanish potato

patience *f* patience (dock); spinach dock

pavot *m* *[Papaver]* poppy; papaver

pavot *m* **de Californie** *[Eschscholtzia californica]* Californian poppy

paysage *m* landscape

pêche *f* peach

pêcher *m* peach tree

pélargonium *m* *[Pelargonium]* pelargonium; geranium

pelle *f* shovel

pelle *f* **ronde** round shovel

pelouse *f* lawn

pennisetum *[Pennisetum]* feather grass; Napier grass; pennisetum

pensée *f* *[Viola]* pansy; viola

penstémon *m* *[Pentstemon]* beard tongue; pentstemon

pépin *m* seed (grape, apple etc), pip

pépinière *f* nursery

pépinière *f* fruitière tree nursery

pépinière *f*; garden-centre *m* garden centre

pépiniériste *m* nurseryman

perce-neige *m, inv* *[Galanthus nivalis]* snowdrop; galanthus

perce-oreille *m* earwig

pergola *f*; pergole *f* pergola

péricarpe *m* seed pod

périr *v* de moississure d'excès d'humidité to damp off (seedlings)

persil *m* parsley

pervenche *f* *[Vinca]* periwinkle; vinca

pesse *f* *[Hippuris]* mare's tail; hippuris

pesticide *m* pesticide

pétale *m* petal

pétasite *m* *[Petasites]* winter heliotrope; bog rhubarb; butterbur; petasites

petit houx *m* *[Ruscus]* butcher's broom, ruscus

petite oseille *f* *[Oxalis]* wood sorrel

pétunia *m* *[Petunia]* petunia

peuplier *m* *[Populus alba]* white poplar; Abele poplar

peuplier *m* d'Italie *[Populus nigra 'italica']* Lombardy poplar

peuplier *m* tremble; tremble *m* *[Populus tremula]* European aspen

phacélie *f* *[Phacelia]* wild heliotrope; phacelia

phalangère *f* à fleur de lis *[Anthericum]* St. Bernard's lily

phaséole *f* haricot bean

phlomide *f* *[Phlomis]* Jerusalem sage; phlomis

phlox *m, inv* *[Phlox]* phlox

phosphate *m* phosphate

phosphore *m* phosphorus

photinia *[Photinia]* photinia

pic *m* pick; pickaxe

pic *m* à tranche mattock

pied-d'alouette *m* *[Delphinium]* larkspur; delphinium

pied-de-chèvre *m* *[Pimpinella saxifraga]* burnet saxifrage

pied-de-veau *m* *[Arum]* cuckoopint; lords and ladies; arum

pied *m* mère stool; rootstock

piège *m* trap; snare

pigamon *m*; pigamon *m* des prés *[Thalictrum]* meadow rue; meadow rhubarb; thalictrum

piment *m* [Capsicum] capsicum; red pepper

pin *m* *[Pinus]* pine

pin *m* de montagne *[Pinus]* mountain pine

pin *m* dur *[Pinus rigida]* *[Pinus palustris]* pitch pine; northern pine

pin *m* sylvestre *[Pinus sylvestris]* Scots pine; Scotch pine

pin *m* maritime *[Pinus]* maritime pine

pincer *v* to pinch; to tip

pioche *f* mattock (point and hoe); pickaxe (two points)

piocheuse *f* digger

piquet *m* peg; stake; post

piqûre *f* insect bite or sting; prick (of thorn)

piqûre *f* d'ortie nettle sting

pissenlit *m* *[Taraxacum]* dandelion

pittosporum *m* *[Pittosporum]* tree daphne; pittosporum

pivoine *f* *[Paeonia]* peony

pivot *m*; racine *f* pivotante taproot

planche *f* bed; flower bed

plant *m*; jeune plant *m* seedling; young plant

plant *m* à repiquer bedding(-out) plant

plant *m* de légumes vegetable plot; vegetable patch

plantage *m* planting; patch of ground under cultivation

plantain *m* *[Plantago]* plantain

plantain *m* d'eau *[Alisma]* water plantain; alisma

plantatation *f* planting

plante *f* plant

plante *f* à fleurs flowering plant

plante *f* annuelle annual plant

plante *f* annuelle résistante au gel hardy annual

plante *f* bisannuelle biennial plant

plante *f* d'appartement pot plant; house plant

plante *f* d'ornement ornamental plant

plante *f* de serre greenhouse plant; glasshouse plant; hothouse plant

plante *f* en pot pot plant
plante *f* frileuse plant sensitive to cold
plante *f* grasse succulent (plant)
plante *f* grimpante climbing plant;
climber; creeper
plante *f* hybride hybrid plant
plante *f* potagère vegetable or herb
plante *f* rampante trailing plant
plante *f* verte potted plant; house plant
plante *f* vivace hardy perennial;
perennial
planter *v* to plant
plantoir *m* dibber; dibble
plantoir *m* à bulbes bulb dibber; bulb
dibble
platane *m* [Platanus] plane tree
plate-bande *f* flower bed; grass border;
border
plate-bande *f* de pépinière nursery bed
platycodon [Platycodon] Chinese
bellflower
platystémon *m* [Platystemon]
Californian poppy; platystemon
plumbago *m*; plombago *m*; plumbago *m*
du Cap [Plumbago capensis]
plumbago; leadwort; Cape leadwort
poinsettie *f* [Euphorbia] poinsettia;
euphorbia
poire *f* pear
poireau *m* leek
poirier *m* [Pyrus] pear tree
poirier *m* d'ornement [Pyrus]
ornamental pear; pyrus
pois *m* pea
pois *m* de senteur [Lathyrus odoratus]
sweet pea
pois *m* vivace everlasting pea
poivron *m* sweet pepper; pimento
pollen *m* pollen
pollinisation *f* pollination
polliniser *v* to pollinate
polygale *m* commun [Polygala]
polygala; milkwort
polythène *m* polythene
pomelo *m* pomelo; grapefruit
pomme *f* rose (of hose or watering can);
cone (eg of pine)
pomme *f* apple
pomme *f* de terre [Solanum tuberosum]
potato
pomme *f* de terre de semence seed
potato
pomme *f* sauvage crab apple
pommier *m* apple tree
pommier *m* à fleurs [Malus] flowering
crab apple tree; malus
pommier-cerise *m* [Malus floribunda]
flowering crab; Japanese crab
pommier *m* sauvage [Malus sylvestris]
crab apple tree; wild crab apple tree
pompe *f* pump
pompon *m* pompom; pompon
porte-greffe *m,inv* stock (for graft);
rootstock; understock
portillon *m* gate
pot *m* à fleurs flowerpot
potamot *m* pondweed; water spike
potasse *f* potash
potassium *m* potassium
poteau *m* post
potée *f* potful, pot
potentille *f* [Potentilla] cinquefoil;
potentilla
potiron *m* pumpkin
poudreuse *f* duster (for insecticides)
pourpier *m* [Portulaca] purslane;
portulaca
pourri *adj* rotten (fruit)
pourrissement *m* rot; rotting; decay
pourriture *f* rot; decay
pourriture *f* grise grey mould
pourriture *f* humide wet rot
pourriture *f* sèche dry rot
pousse *f* sprout; young shoot
pousse *f* terminale top shoot; terminal
shoot
pousser *v* to grow; to shoot; to sprout
précoce *adj* early (eg potato)
prêle *f*; préle *f* [Equisetum] horsetail;
equisetum
prendre *v* racine to strike roots
primevère *f* [Primula] primula; primrose
primevère *f* commune [Primula]
cowslip
primevère *f* à grandes fleurs [Primula]
primrose
primevère *f* des champs [Primula]
cowslip

primevère *f* des jardins *[Primula;
Polyanthus]* polyanthus
printanier,-ière *adj* spring
printemps *m* spring
producteur *m* vegetable grower
producteur *m* de bulbes bulb grower
producteur *m* de fruits fruit grower; fruit
farmer
produits *mpl* maraîchers market garden
produce
profondeur *f* depth
propagation *f* propagation
propagation *f* par drageons
propagation by root cuttings
prune *f* plum
prune *f* de Damas damson
prunelle *f* sloe
prunellier *m*; épine *f* noire *[Prunus
spinosa]* blackthorn; sloe bush
prunier *m* *[Prunus]* plum tree
prunier *m* à fleurs *[Prunus]* flowering
plum; prunus
prunier *m* cérasifère *[Prunus cerasifera]*
cherry plum
prunier *m* de Damas damson tree
pseudococcus *m* mealy bug
puceron *m* noir blackfly
puceron *m* vert; puceron *m* (des
plantes) aphis, greenfly
puits *m* well
pulicaire *f* *[Erigeron]* fleabane; pulicaria,
erigeron
pulmonaire *f* officinale *[Pulmonaria]*
lungwort
pulsatille *f* *[Pulsatilla]* pasque flower
pulvérisateur *m* sprayer; tank sprayer
punaise *f* de la pomme de terre *[Lygus
pabulinus]* potato capsid bug
puschkinia *[Puschkinia]* striped squill;
puschkinia
pyrale *f* pyralis; meal moth; bee moth
pyrale *f* des pommes codling moth
pyrole *f* *[Pyrola]* wintergreen
quenouille *f* 1 quenouille-trained fruit
tree; 2 cat's tail; reed mace; bulrush
quenouille *f* de Cléopâtre *[Eremurus]*
fox tail; eremurus
queue-de-renard *f* *[Amaranthus]* love-
lies-bleeding

R

rabattage *m* cutting back (shoots,
branch)
rabattre *v* to cut back (shoots, branch
etc)
racine *f* root
radicelle *f* radicle; rootlet
radis *m* *[Raphanus sativus]* radish
radis *m* à cheval *[Cochlearia armoracia]*
[Armoracia rusticana] horseradish
radis noir black (winter) radish
raifort *m* horseradish
raisin *m* d'ours *[Arctostaphylos]*
bearberry; arctostaphylos
raisin *m*; grain *m* de raisin grape
rame *f* stick; prop (for peas, etc); branch
(of tree)
rame *f* pour haricots bean-stick
rameau *m* branch; bough; twig
rameau *m* à bois long shoot
rameau *m* en fleurs spray of blossom
raquette *f* *[Opuntia]* prickly pear; nopal
rat *m* rat
ratière *f*; piège *m* à rats rat trap
râteau *m* rake
râteau *m* à foin hay rake
râteau-faneur *m* tedder rake; side-
delivery rake
ratissage *m* raking
ratisser *v* to rake; to rake up (leaves); to
rake over (flower bed)
ratisser *v* (eg une allée) to hoe (eg a
path)
ratissoire *f* scuffle hoe, Dutch hoe
ravalement *m* cutting back; lopping
ravaler *v* to cut back; to lop
rave *f* de campagne *[Cochlearia
armoracia]*, horseradish
ravenelle *f* 1 wallflower; 2 wild radish
récolte *f* crop (of fruit etc); harvest;
harvesting (grain)
récolte *f* améliorante crop that enriches
the soil
règne *m* végétal plant kingdom;
vegetable kingdom
regreffer *v* to top graft

reine-claude *f* greengage
reine-marguerite *f* *[Callistephus]* China aster
rejet *m* shoot
remembrement *m* des terres re-allocation or regrouping of land
remise *f* shed; outhouse
remontant *adj* perpetual flowering; remontant
remorque *f* trailer
remorque *f* (câble de) towrope
rempotage *m* repotting; potting on
rempoter *v* to repot
renard *m* fox
renoncule *f* *[Ranunculus]* buttercup; garden buttercup; ranunculus
renoncule *f* à feuilles d'aconit *[Ranunculus]* fair-maids-of-France; fair-maids-of-Kent;
renoncule *f* des champs *[Ranunculus]* corn crowfoot; ranunculus
renoncule *f* double *[Ranunculus]* batchelor's buttons
renouée *f* *[Polygonum]* polygonum; knotgrass; knotweed
renouée *f* de Turkestan *[Polygonum baldschaunicum]* Russian vine
rentrer *v* la recolte to gather in the harvest; to gather in the crops
repiquage *m* pricking out; planting out; bedding out
repiquer *v* to prick out (seedlings), to bed out (plants)
replanter *v* to replant
réséda *m* odorant *[Reseda]* mignonette, reseda
résineux *m, inv* conifer
résistant *adj* au gel hardy (plant)
rhizome *m* rootstock; rhizome
rhododendron *m* *[Rhododendron]* rhododendron
rhubarbe *f* rhubarb
ricin *m* *[Ricinus]* castor-oil plant
robinier *m* *[Robinia]* false acacia; locust tree; robinia
rocaille *f* rockery; rock garden
rodgersia *[Rodgersia]* rodgersia
rodonticide *m* rodent killer
romaine *f* cos lettuce

romarin *m* *[Rosmarinus officinalis]* rosemary; rosmarinus
ronce *f*; ronce *f* des haies; mûrier *m* sauvage *[Rubus fruticosus]* blackberry; bramble
ronce *f*; roncier *m*; roncière *f* bramble; bramble bush; blackberry bush
ronce *f* bleu *[Rubus caesius]* dewberry
roquette *f* *[Eruca sativa]* rocket; garden rocket; Roman rocket
roquette *f* de mer sea rocket
roquette *f* des champs corn rocket
rose *f* *[Rosa]* rose; rosa
rose d'Inde *[Tagetes erecta]* African marigold
rose *f* de chien *[Rosa canina]* wild rose; dog rose
rose *f* de Jéricho *[Anastatica]* rose of Jericho; resurrection plant
rose *f* de Noël *[Helleborus]* Christmas rose
rose *f* de Notre-Dame *[Paeonia]* peony
rose *f* des quatre saisons *[Rosa]* monthly rose; Indian rose; China rose
rose *f* incarnate *[Rosa damascena]* damask rose
rose *f* mousseuse *[Rosa centifolia muscosa]* moss rose
rose *f* musquée musk rose
rose *f* pivoine *[Paeonia]* double peony
rose *f* pompon *[Rosa]* fairy rose; pompom rose; button rose
rose *f* trémière *[Althaea rosea]* hollyhock; rose mallow
rose-thé *f* *[Rosa]* tea rose
roseau *m* commun *[Arundo Phragmites]* reed; common reed-grass
rosée *f* de soleil *[Drosera]* sundew
roseraie *f* rose garden
rosiériste *m,f* rose grower
rosier *m* rosebush; rose tree
rosier *m* demi-tige half-standard rose
rosier *m* floribunda floribunda rose bush
rosier *m* grimpant climbing rose; rambler rose
rosier *m* nain; rosier miniature dwarf rose
rosier *m* parasol parasol rose; umbellate rose

rosier *m* **pleureur** weeping rose
rosier *m* **polyantha** polyantha rose
rosier *m* **remontant** perpetual flowering rose
rosier *m* **sarmenteux** rambler rose
rosier *m* **tige; rosier à tige; rosier sur tige; rosier haute tige** standard rose
rossolis *m* *[Drosera]* sundew
rotation *f* **des cultures** rotation of crops
rouille *f* rust; blight (rose, cereal)
rouleau *m* roller
ruban *m* **de bergère** *[Phalaris]* ribbon grass; gardener's garters; phalaris
ruche *f* beehive
rudbeckie *f* *[Rudbeckia hirta]* rudbeckia; cone flower; yellow daisy
rue *f* *[Ruta]* rue
rue *f* **des prés** *[Thalictrum]* meadow rue, meadow rhubarb
rustique *adj* hardy (plant); rustic
rutabaga *m* swede; Swedish turnip

S

sable *m* sand
sable *m* **gras** loamy sand
sabline *f* *[Arenaria]* sandwort
sabot *m* **de la Vierge** *[Cypripedium]* lady's slipper orchid
sabot *m* **de Vénus** *[Cypripedium]* lady's slipper orchid
sabots *mpl* **de jardin** garden shoes
sachet *m* **de graines** packet of seed
safran *m* *[Crocus sativus]* saffron; crocus
safran *m* **bâtard** *[Carthamus]* safflower; dyer's saffron
safran *m* **cultivé; safran** *m* **officinal** *[Crocus]* autumn-flowering crocus
safran *m* **printanier** *[Crocus albiflorus]* spring crocus
saignée *f* drainage ditch
sainfoin *m* *[Onobrychis]* sainfoin
sainfoin *m* **à bouquets** *[Hedysarum]* French honeysuckle
sainfoin *m* **d'Espagne** *[Hedysarum]* French honeysuckle
saintpaulia *f* *[Saintpaulia]* African violet; saintpaulia
salicaire *f* **commune** *[Lythrum]* purple loosestrife; lythrum
salpiglossis *m* *[Salpiglossis]* salpiglossis
salsifis *m* salsify
salvia *f* *[Salvia]* salvia
sans épines *adj* thornless
sans pépins *adj* seedless
santoline *f* *[Santolina]* lavender cotton; santolina
sanvitalia *[Sanvitalia]* sanvitalia
sapin *m* *[Abies]* fir
sapin *m* **de l'Oregon** *[Pseudotsuga menziesii]* Douglas fir; Oregon pine
sapin *m* **de Norvège; sapin blanc** *[Picea abies]* Norway spruce; white fir
saponaire *f* *[Saponaria]* soapwort; saponaria
sarclage *m* weeding
sarcler *v* to weed
sarclage *m* **(de mauvaises herbes)** hoeing (weeds)
sarcler *v* **(les mauvaises herbes)** to hoe (weeds)
sarcloir *m* weeding hoe
sarracénie *f* *[Sarracenia]* sarracenia; side-saddle flower; pitcher plant
sarriette *f* *[Satureia montana]* savory; winter savory
satin *m* **blanc** *[Lunaria]* honesty; white satin
sauge *f* sage
sauge *f* **à fleurs rouges** *[Salvia]* salvia
sauge *f* **amère; sauge des bois** bitter sage; wood sage
sauge *f* **sauvage; sauge des prés** meadow sage
sauge *f* **sclarée** clary
saule *m* *[Salix]* willow
saule *m* **blanc; saule** *m* **argenté** *[Salix alba]* white willow, silver willow
saule *m* **cassant; saule** *m* **fragile** *[Salis fragilis]* crack willow; brittle willow
saule *m* **marsault; marsault** *m* *[Salix caprea]* goat willow; pussy willow; sallow; grey willow
saule *m* **pleureur** weeping willow

sauvageon *m* 1 wild stock (for grafting) 2 sucker; 3 wilding; seedling

saxifrage *f* [*Saxifraga*] saxifrage

saxifrage *f* d'automne [*Saxifraga aizoides*] yellow saxifrage

saxifrage *f* dorée [*Chrysoplenium*] golden saxifrage, chrysoplenium

saxifrage *f* mousseuse [*Saxifraga*] mossy saxifrage

saxifrage *f* ombreuse [*Saxifraga*] London pride; saxifrage

scabieuse *f* [*Scabiosa*] scabious; sweet scabious

scarificateur *m* scarifier

scarole *f* broad leaved endive

sceau *m* de Salomon [*Polygonatum*] Solomon's seal, polygonatum

scie *f* à bois wood saw

scie *f* à bûches bow saw; log saw; tree saw; bucksaw

scie *f* à chaine chainsaw

scie *f* d'élagage pruning saw

scille *f* [*Scilla*] scilla; squill; bluebell

scion *m* scion

scirpe *m* [*Scirpus*] club rush; scirpus

sclarée *f* [*Salvia sclarea*] clary

scolopendre *f* centipede; scolopendra

sécateur *m* secateur; (pair of) secateurs; pruning shears

sécateur (*m*) à deux mains two handed secateur; long-handeled lopper

sécheresse *f* drought; dryness

semelle *f* à fruits punnet

semence *f* seed

semer *v* to sow (seed)

semer *v* à claire-voie to sow thinly

semis *m* 1 sowing; 2 seedbed, seedplot; 3 seedling

semoir *m* seeding machine; sowing machine

semoir *m* à engrais seed and fertilizer drill

semoir *m* à main hand seeder

semoir *m* mécanique seeding machine; sowing machine

séneçon *m* [*Senecio*] groundsel; ragwort

serfouage *m* hoeing

serfouette *f* combined hoe and fork

serfouir *v* to hoe; to loosen (the soil)

serfouir *v* les plantes potagères to hoe vegetables

serfouissage *m*; serfouage *m* (de plantes potagères) hoeing (vegetables)

seringa *m*; seringat *m* [*Philadelphus*] syringa; mock orange; philadelphus

serpe *f* 1 pruning knife; 2 billhook

serpette *f* pruning knife

serre *f* greenhouse; glasshouse

serre *f* froide unheated greenhouse, cold house

sève *f* sap

sidalcée *f*; sidalcea *m* [*Sidalcea*] Greek mallow; sidalcea

silène *m* [*Silene*] catchfly; silene

sillonneur *m* drill plough

silo *m* de pommes de terre clamp of potatoes, potato clamp

silo-couloir bunker silo

skimmia [*Skimmia*] skimmia

soissons *m* haricot bean; kidney bean

sol *m* soil; earth

sol *m* argileux clayey soil

sol *m* crayeux chalky soil

sol *m* détrempé sodden soil; waterlogged soil

sol *m* pierreux stony soil

sol *m* sablonneux sandy soil

sol *m* tourbeux peaty soil

solanacée *f* [*Solanum*] solanum

soldanelle *f* [*Soldanella*] moonwort

soleil *m*; soleil vivace [*Helianthus*] sunflower

solidage *f* [*Solidago*] solidago; golden rod

sorbier *m* commun; sorbier des oiseaux; sorbier des oiseleurs; sorbier sauvage [*Sorbus aucuparia*] rowan tree; mountain ash

sorgho *m* sorghum; Indian millet

souche *f* root stock, stump (tree, etc), vine stock

souci *m* [*Calendula*] marigold; pot-marigold

souci *m* des jardins [*Calendula*] marigold; Scotch marigold; pot-marigold, calendula

soufre *m* sulphur; sulfur

source *f* spring (water)

souricière *f* mousetrap

souris *f* mouse

spirée *f* *[Spiraea]* spiraea

statice *m* *[Statice Limonium]* sea lavender; sea thrift; sea pink, statice

stokesia *[Stokesia]* Stoke's aster; stokesia

stolon *m* runner; sucker

succulent *adj* succulent

sulfate *m* d'ammoniaque ammonium sulphate; ammonium sulfate

sulfate *m* de cuivre copper sulphate; copper sulfate

sumac *m* *[Rhus]* sumach; rhus

sumac *m* vénéneux *[Rhus]* poison ivy; poison sumac

superphosphate *m* de chaux superphosphate of lime; calcium superphosphate

supprimer *v* to remove; to cut off (eg dead flowers)

sureau *m* *[Sambucus]* elder

sureau *m* noir *[Sambucus nigra]* common elder

surface *f* plantée en vergers area under fruit; orchard area

surfleurir *v* to flower again (in same year)

surgeon *m* sucker

surgreffage *m* intergrafting

surmûri *adj* overripe

sycomore *m* *[Acer pseudoplatanus]* sycamore

sylvie *f* *[Anemone]* wood anemone

symphorine *f* *[Symphoricarpos]* snowberry; St. Peter's wort; symphoricarpos

T

tabac *m* d'ornement *[Nicotiana]* tobacco plant

tagète *m* *[Tagetes]* French marigold; African marigold; tagetes

taille *f* pruning

taille *f* d'hiver winter pruning

taille *f* en sec winter pruning

taille *f* en vert; taille d'été summer pruning

taille *f* fruitière spur pruning

taille *f* ornamentale des arbres topiary

taille-bordures *m* edger; powered edger

taille-haies *m* hedgetrimmer; hedge-cutter

tailler *v* to prune (bush, tree); to trim

taillis *m* coppice; copse

tamaris *m* *[Tamarix]* tamarisk; tamarix

tanaisie *f* *[Tanacetum]* tansy

tardif, -ive *adj* late (eg potato)

taupe *f* mole

taupin *m* spring beetle; click beetle

tavelure *f* scab; spots; speckles (on fruit)

tégument *m* tegument; seed coat

terrain *m* pierreux stony ground

terrautage *m* composting

terre *f* ground; soil, earth, land

terre *f* argileuse; terre limoueuse clay soil; argillaceous soil

terre *f* calcaire chalky soil

terre *f* de bruyère heath soil; heather soil; heath mould

terre *f* émiettée garden soil; fine earth

terre *f* franche vegetable mould; garden mould

terre *f* glaise clay

terre *f* riche rich soil

terre *f* sableuse sandy soil

terre *f* végétale mould; loam

terreau *m* mould (vegetable); humus; compost; potting compost, garden mould; black earth

terreau *m* de feuilles leaf mould; compost

terreau *m* enrichi pour bulbes bulb fibre

terreau *m* horticole horticultural compost

terreau *m* rempotage potting compost; potting soil

terreautage *m* distribution of vegetable mould to the ground

terreauter *v* to treat with mould (plant, ground)

terrer *v* to earth up

terroir *m* soil; ground; earth

tête *f* de dragon *[Dracocephalum]* dragon's head

théier *m* *[Camellia]* tea plant
thlaspi *m* *[Iberis]* candytuft; iberis; thlaspi
thlaspi *m* **des champs** *[Thlaspi]* pennycress
thlaspi *m* **jaune** *[Alyssum]* rock alyssum
thrips *m* thrips
thuia *m*; **thuya** *m* *[Thuya]* thuya; thuja; arbor vitae
thunbergie *f* *[Thunbergia]* thunbergia
thym *m* thyme
tiarella *m*; **tiarelle** *f* *[Tiarella]* foam flower; tiarella
tige *f* stem; stalk (of plant)
tilleul *m* *[Tilia x europea]* linden tree; lime tree; European lime
tilleul *m* **à grandes feuilles** *[Tilia platyphyllos]* large-leaved lime
tilleul *m* **à petites feuilles** *[Tilia cordata]* small-leaved lime
tipule *f* cranefly
tire-racines *m* weeder
tithonia *[Tithonia]* Mexican sunflower
tomate *f* tomato
tomate *f* **cerise** cherry tomato
tondaison *f* mowing
tondeuse *f*; **tondeuse** *f* **à gazon** mower; grass cutter
tondeuse *f* **à moteur** motor mower
tondeuse *f* **autoportée** sit-on lawn mower
tondeuse *f* **électrique** electric mower
tondeuse *f* **mécanique** hand mower
tondeuse *f* **sur coussin d'air** hover mower
tondeuse *f* **thermique** petrol engine mower
tondre *v* 1 to mow (lawn, grass); 2 to shear or clip
tonte *f* 1 mowing; 2 clipping (tree, hedge)
tontine *f* protective sacking (round roots of trees for transpantation)
tontiner *v* to ball and burlap
topiare *f* topiary
topinambour *m* *[Helianthus tuberosus]* Jerusalem artichoke
tourbe *f* peat
tournesol *m* *[Helianthus]* sunflower
tracteur *m* tractor

tradescantie *f* **de Virginie** *[Tradescantia]* tradescantia; spiderwort
transplantoir *m* 1 garden trowel; 2 transplanter; transplanting machine
trèfle *m* clover
treillage *m* trellis; trellising
tremper *v* to soak; to drench
trientale *f* **d'Europe** *[Trientalis]* wintergreen, starflower
trinitaire *f* *[Hepatica]* liverwort
trisannuel *adj* triennial
tritome *m* *[Kniphofia]* red-hot poker; torch lily; kniphofia
troène *m* *[Ligustrum]* privet; ligustrum
trognon *m* core (eg of apple)
trognon *m* **de chou** cabbage stump; cabbage stalk
trolle *m* *[Trollius]* globe flower; trollius
tronc *m* **d'arbre** trunk; tree trunk
tronçonneuse *f* **electrique** chainsaw (electric)
tronçonneuse *f* **thermique** chainsaw (petrol engine)
tubéreuse *f* *[Polyanthes]* tuberose
tubercule *m* tuber
tubérisation *f* formation of tubers
tue-chien *m*, *inv* 1 *[Solanum nigrum]* black nightshade; 2 *[Colchicum autumnale]* meadow saffron
tulipe *f* *[Tulipa]* tulip
tulipier *m* tulip tree
tussilage *m*; **pas d'âne** *[Tussilago]* coltsfoot
tuteur *m* stake; prop; support
tuteurage *m* staking (of plants)
tuteurer *v* to stake
tuyau *m* **d'arrosage** hose; garden hose
tuyau *m* **perforé** sprinkler hose

V

valériane *f* *[Valeriana]* valerian
valériane *f* **grecque bleue** *[Polemonium]* Jacob's ladder; Greek valerian, polemonium

vaporisateur *m* sprayer
variété *f* variety
variété *f* **cultivée** cultivar
variété *f* **hybride** hybrid variety
veilleuse *f* *[Colchicum]* meadow saffron
velvote *f* *[Linaria]* toadflax
vendange *f* grape harvest
vendanger *v* to harvest grapes
vendanger, machine *f* **à** mechanical
  grape harvester
vendangeur, euse *m,f* grape picker
ver *m* **blanc** cockchafer grub
ver *m* **de terre** worm; earthworm
ver m des moissons cutworm
ver *m* **du bois** wood worm
vératre *m* *[Veratrum]* false hellebore;
  white hellebore
véreux *adj* maggoty
verge *f* **d'or** *[Solidago]* golden rod;
  solidago
verger *m* orchard
vergerette *f* *[Erigeron]* fleabane;
  erigeron
verne *m*; **vergne** *m* [Alnus glutinosa]
  alder
véronique *f* *[Veronica]* veronica;
  speedwell
verveine *f* *[Verbena]* verbena; vervain
victoria *f* **regia** *[Victoria]* royal water lily
vigne *f*; **vigne** *f* **à raisin** vine; grapevine
vigne *f* **d'ornement** *[Vitis]* ornamental
  vine; vitis
vigne-vierge *f* *[Parthenocissus]* Virginia
  creeper; American ivy; parthenocissus
vignoble *m* vineyard
violette *f* *[Viola]* violet
violette *f* **de jardin** *[Viola]* viola; pansy
violette *f* **de Marie** *[Campanula]*
  campanula; Canterbury bell
violette *f* **de Parme** *[Viola]* Parma violet
violier *m* *[Matthiola]* stock; gillyflower
violier *m* **jaune** *[Cheiranthus]* wallflower
viorne *f* *[Viburnum]* viburnum
vipérine *f* *[Echium]* viper's bugloss
vitex *m* *[Vitex]* agnus castus; chaste
  tree; vitex
viticulture *f* vine-growing
vivace *adj* perennial; hardy; long-lived
volis *m* wind break

volubile *adj* twining
volubilis *m* *[Ipomaea]* convolvulus;
  morning glory; ipomaea
vrille *f* tendril

WYZ

waldsteinia *[Waldsteinia]* barren
  strawberry; waldsteinia
weigelie *f* *[Weigela or Diervilla]* weigela;
  bush honeysuckle
wistarie *f* *[Wistaria]* wisteria; wistaria
yucca *m* *[Yucca]* yucca
zinnia *m* *[Zinnia]* zinnia

A

Aaron's beard *[Hypericum]* millepertuis *m* velu
Aaron's rod; verbascum *[Verbascum]* bouillon-blanc *m*
abelia *[Abelia]* abélie *f*
acacia acacia *m*
acaena *[Acaena]* acaena *f*
acanthus *[Acanthus]* acanthe *f*
acarid; acaridan acarien *m*
achillea; yarrow; milfoil *[Achillea millefolium]* achillée *f* millefeuille
aconitum *[Aconitum]* aconit *m*
acorus *[Acorus]* acore *m*
actinidia *[Actinidia]* actinidia
adiantum *[Adiantum]* adiante *m*
adonis *[Adonis]* adonis *f*; goutte-de-sang *f*
aerator; lawn aerator aérateur *m*
African lily *[Agapanthus]* agapanthe *m*
African marigold *[Tagetes erecta]* rose *f* d'Inde; tagète *m*
African violet *[Saintpaulia]* saintpaulia *f*
agapanthus *[Agapanthus]* agapanthe *m*
agathaea *[Agathaea]* agathée *f* amelloïde
ageratum *[Ageratum]* agérate *m*; ageratum *m*
agnus castus *[Vitex]* vitex *m*
agricultural lime chaux *f* agricole
agrostemma *[Agrostemma]* agrostemme *f* en couronne
agrostis *[Agrostis]* agrostide *f*; agrostis *m*
akebia *[Akebia]* akebia
alchemilla *[Alchemilla]* alchémille *f*
alder, common *[Alnus glutinosa]* aune/aulne *m* glutineux; verne *m*; vergne *m*
alder, grey; alder, European *[Alnus incana]* aune/aulne *m* blanc
Alexandrian laurel *[Danae]* laurier *m* d'Alexandrie
alkanet; anchusa *[Anchusa]* buglosse *f*
allium; ornamental allium *[Allium]* ail *m* décoratif
alluvial limoneux, -euse *adj*
almond amande *f*
almond tree *[Prunus dulcis]* amandier *m*
aloe aloès *m*
Alpine aster *[Aster alpinus]* aster *m* des Alpes; aster alpin
Alpine bartsia *[Bartsia alpina]* bartschia des Alpes
Alpine laburnum cytise *m* des Alpes
alum root *[Heuchera]* heuchère *f*
alyssum *[Alyssum]* alysse *f*; alysson *m*; corbeille *f* d'argent
amaranthus *[Amaranthus]* amarante *f* à fleurs en queue
amaryllis amaryllis *f*
amaryllis belladonna *[Amaryllis]* lis *m* de Saint-Jacques
ambrosia; wormseed ambroisie *f*
ammonium sulphate; ammonium sulfate sulfate *m* d'ammoniaque
anagallis *[Anagallis]* anagallide *f*
anaphalis *[Anaphalis]* bouton *m* d'argent
anemone *[Anemone]* anémone *f*
angelica *[Angelica]* angélique *f*; angélique *f* de Bohême; herbe-aux-anges *f*
animated oat *[Avena]* avoine *f* d'ornement
annual mulch paillis *m* annuel
annual (plant) annuelle *f*
ant fourmi *f*
ant destroying; ant killing antifourmis *adj*
ant's nest; ant hill fourmilière *f*
anthemis *[Anthemis]* camomille *f*
anthurium; flamingo plant *[Anthurium]* anthure *m*
antirrhinum *[Antirrhinum]* antirrhine *f*; muflier *m*; gueule-de-loup *f*
aphis puceron *m* vert; aphis *m*
aphis; aphids; plant-lice aphidés *mpl*; aphidiens (mpl)
apple pomme *f*
apple capsid bug capside *f* du pommier
apple tree pommier *m*
apricot abricot *m*
apricot tree abricotier *m*

aquilegia *[Aquilegia]* ancolie *f*; aquilegia *f*; aquilégie *f*

arable land labourage *m*

arabis *[Arabis]* arabis *f*; arabette *f*

arbor vitae *[Thuya]* thuia *m*; thuya *m*

arctotis *[Arctotis]* arctotis

area under fruit; orchard area surface *f* plantée en vergers

arenaria *[Arenaria]* arénaire *f*

aristolochia *[Aristolochia]* aristoloche *f*

armeria *[Armeria]* armeria *f*; armérie *f*; armeria *f* commune; gazon *m* d'Espagne

arnica; mountain arnica *[Arnica montana]* arnica *f* des montagnes; arnique *f* des montagnes; bétoine *f* des montagnards; bétoine des Vosges

arrow head *[Sagittaria]* flèche *f* d'eau

artemesia *[Artemesia]* armoise *f*

artichoke, globe *[Cynara scolymus]* artichaut *m*

artichoke, Jerusalem *[Helianthus tuberosus]* hélianthe *m* tubéreux

artificial fertilizer engrais *m* chimique

arum *[Arum]* gouet *m* d'Italie; pied-de-veau *m*

aruncus *[Aruncus]* barbe-de-bouc *f*

asarabacca *[Asarum]* cabaret *m*

asarum *[Asarum]* asaret *m*

ash, common; ash, European *[Fraxinus excelsior]* frêne *m* commun

asparagus asperges *fpl*

asparagus bed aspergerie *f*; aspergière *f*

asparagus beetle crocère *m* de l'asperge

aspen, European *[Populus tremula]* peuplier *m* tremble; tremble *m*

asperula *[Asperula]* aspérule *f* odorante

asphodel *[Asphodelus luteus]* bâton *m* royal; bâton *m* de Jacob

asphodel *[Asphodelus]* asphodèle *m*

asphodeline *[Asphodeline]* asphodèle *m* blanc

aster *[Aster]* aster *m*

aubergine *[Aubergine]* aubergine *f*

aubretia *[Aubretia]* aubrétie *f*; aubretia *f*

aucuba *[Aucuba]* aucuba *m* de Japon

auricula *[Primula auricula]* auricule *f*

Austrian flax *[Linum]* lin *m* d'Autriche

autumn automne *m*

autumn bells *[Gentiana]* gentiane *f* des marais

autumn crocus; meadow saffron *[Colchicum]* veilleuse *f*; tue-chien *m,inv*; colchique *m* automnal

autumn flowering crocus *[Crocus]* safran *m* cultivé; safran *m* officinal

avens; geum *[Geum]* benoîte *f*

axe hache *f*

azalea *[Rhododendron; Azalea]* azalée *f*

azalea japonica *[Azalea japonica]* azalée *f* de Japon

azalea mollis *[Azalea mollis]* azalée *f* de Chine

B

bald cypress; swamp cypress; taxodium *[Taxodium]* cyprès *m* chauve

ball and burlap (to) tontiner *v*

balsam apple *[Momordica balsamina]* momordique *f* balsamique

bamboo *[Bamboo]* bambou *m*

barberry *[Berberis]* berbéris *m* commun

barbeton daisy *[Gerbera]* gerbéra

bark (of tree) écorce *f*

barren strawberry *[Waldsteinia]* waldsteinia

barrenwort *[Epimedium]* épimède *f*

basil *[Ocimum basilicum]* basilic *m*; herbe *f* royale; oranger *m* du savetier

basket; hand basket panier *m*

batchelor's buttons *[Ranunculus]* renoncule *f* double

bay laurel; noble laurel *[Laurus nobilis]* laurier *m* commun; laurier noble; laurier d'Apollon; laurier-sauce *m*

bean see broad, French, haricot, runner, scarlet

bean-stick rame *f* pour haricots

bear's breeches *[Acanthus]* acanthe *f*

bear's ear *[Primula auricula]* oreille *f* d'ours; auricule *f*

bear's foot *[Acanthus]* acanthe *f*

bear's foot; green hellebore *[Helleborus viridis]* ellébore *m* vert; hellébore vert

bearberry *[Arctostaphyllos]* raisin *m*

d'ours

bearbind; bindweed *[Calystegia]* liseron *m* des haies

beard tongue; pentstemon *[Pentstemon]* penstémon *m*

bed planche *f*

bed out (to) (plants) repiquer *v*

bedding out repiquage *m*

bedding(-out) plant plant *m* à repiquer

bee; honey bee abeille *f*

bee moth pyrale *f*

beech *[Fagus sylvatica]* hêtre *m* (commun); fayard *m*; fouteau *m*

beehive ruche *f*

beet; beetroot betterave *f*

begonia *[Begonia]* bégonia *m*; bégonie *f*

bell-flower *[Campanula]* campanule *f*

belladonna *[Atropa belladonna]* belladone *f*

belladonna lily *[Amaryllis]* lis *m* de Saint-Jacques

bent grass *[Agrostis]* agrostide *f*; agrostis *m*

berberis *[Berberis]* berbéris *m*; épine-vinette *f*

bergamot tree bergamotier *m*

berry baie *f*

besom balai *m*

betony *[Betonica]* bétoine *f*

bidens; burr marigold *[Bidens]* bidens *m*

biennial bisannuel,-elle *adj*

biennual (plant) bisannuelle *f*

biennial plant plante *f* bisannuelle

bignonia *[Bignonia]* bignone *f*; bignonia *m*

bilberry; blueberry myrtille *f*

billhook serpe *f*; courbet *m*; fauchet *m*

birch, downy *[Betula pubescens]* bouleau *m* pubescent

birch, silver *[Betula pendula]* bouleau *m* blanc

birthwort; aristolochia *[Aristolochia]* aristoloche *f*

bitter apple *[Cucurbita]* coloquinte *f*

bitter orange; Seville orange orange *f* amère

bitter orange tree; Seville orange tree *[Citrus]* oranger *m* amère

bitter sage; wood sage sauge *f* amère; sauge des bois

black nightshade *[Solanum nigrum]* tue-chien *m, inv*

black spot disease (roses) maladie *f* des taches noires; marsonia *f*

blackberry mûre *f*

blackberry bush; bramble *[Rubus fruticosus]* mûrier *m* sauvage; ronce *f*; ronce *f* des haies

blackcurrant cassis *m*; groseille *f* noire

blackcurrant bush *[Ribes nigrum]* cassissier *m*; groseillier *m* noir

blackfly puceron *m* noir

blackthorn *[Prunus spinosa]* épine *f* noire; prunellier *m*

bladder-senna *[Colutea]* baguenaudier *m*

blanket flower *[Gaillardia]* gaillarde *f*

blazing star *[Liatris]* liatride *f*

bleeding heart *[Dicentra]* cœur-de-Marie *m*; cœur-de-Jeannette *m*

blight (fruit trees) cloque *f*; cloque du pêcher

blight (rose, cereal) rouille *f*

bloom, in en fleur(s)

bloom; blossom fleur *f*; floraison *f*

blossom (to) être *v* en fleur(s); se couvrir *v* de fleurs

blue bottle *[Centaurea]* centaurée *f* bleuet

blue gentian *[Gentiana]* gentiane *f* de printemps; gentiane printanière

blue marguerite *[Agathaea]* agathée *f* céleste; agathée *f* amelloïde

bluebell *[Hyacinthus]* jacinthe *f* des bois; jacinthe *f* sauvage

bluebell *[Campanula]* campanule *f* à feuilles rondes

bog arum; calla *[Calla]* calla *f* des marais

bog rhubarb *[Petasites]* pétasite *m*

bog violet; butterwort *[Pinguicula]* grassette *f*

boggy marécageux,-euse *adj*

bole (of tree) fût *m*; tronc *m*

bolt (to); go to seed (to) monter *v*; monter en graine

bonsai bonsai *m*

boots, PVC bottes *fpl* PVC

boots, rubber bottes *fpl* en caoutchouc
borage *[Borago]* bourrache *f*
Bordeaux mixture bouillie *f* bordelaise; bouillie *f* cuprique; bouillie *f* cupro-calcique
bougainvillea *[Bougainvillea]* bougainvillée *f*; bougainvillier *m*
bow saw; log saw scie *f* à bûches
box (to); heel in (to) (eg seedlings) mettre *v* en jauge
box, flower caisse *f* de fleurs
box, seed germoir *m*
box, window bac *m* à fleurs
box; box tree *[Buxus]* buis *m*
bramble ronce *f*, roncier *m*; roncière *f*; mûrier *m* sauvage
branch; bough branche *f*, rameau *m*; rame *f*
branch lopper échenilloir *m*
break up (eg clod) (to) émietter *v*
broad bean *[Vicia faba]* fève *f*
broad-leaved feuillu,-e *adj*
broad leaved endive scarole *f*
broccoli brocoli *m*
broom (sweeping) balai *m*
broom; cytisus *[Cytisus]* cytise *m*
broom; genista *[Genista]* genêt *m*
brown rot mildiou *m*
brush (vegetation) brande *f*
brushwood broussaille *f*
Brussels sprouts choux *mpl* de Bruxelles
bucksaw scie *f* à bûches
buckthorn *[Rhamnus]* nerprun *m*
bud (of flower) bouton *m*
bud (of plant, tree) bourgeon *m*; œil *m*
bud (to) (plant, tree) bourgeonner *v*; écussonner *v*
budding écussonnage *m*; greffage *m* en écusson
budding (plant) bourgeonnant *adj*
budding knife écussonnoir *m*
budding; shield graft greffe *f* en écusson
buddleia *[Buddleia]* buddleia *m*; lilas *m* de Chine
bugle *[Ajuga]* bugle *f*
bugloss *[Anchusa]* buglosse *f*
bulb bulbe *m*; oignon *m*
bulb dibber; bulb dibble plantoir *m* à bulbes
bulb fibre terreau *m* enrichi pour bulbes
bulbs for naturalisation bulbes *mpl* à naturaliser
bulb grower producteur *m* de bulbes
bulbil; bulblet; small bulb bulbille *f*
bulrush; reed mace; cat's-tail *[Typha]* massette *f*
bunker silo silo-couloir *m*
bupleurum *[Bupleurum]* buplèvre *m*
burnet saxifrage *[Pimpinella saxifraga]* pied-de-chèvre *m*
Burning Bush *[Dictamnus]* fraxinelle *f*
burst into bloom (to) s'épanouir *v*
bush arbuste *m*
bush tree; low bush tree basse-tige *m*; arbre *m* à basse-tige
butcher's broom *[Ruscus]* fragon *m*; fragon *m* épineux; buis *m* piquant; petit houx *m*; myrte *m* épineux
butterbur; petasites *[Petasites]* pétasite *m*
buttercup; garden buttercup *[Ranunculus]* bouton *m* d'or; renoncule *f*
buxus *[Buxus]* buis *m*

C

cabbage chou *m*
cabbage stump; cabbage stalk trognon *m* de chou
cactus cactus *m*; cactier *m*
calamint *[Calamintha]* calament *m*
calceolaria *[Calceolaria]* calcéolaire *f*
calcium superphosphate superphosphate *m* de chaux
calendula *[Calendula]* souci *m* des jardins
Californian poppy *[Eschscholtzia californica]* eschscholtzie *f*, platystémon *m*; pavot *m* de Californie
callistephus *[Callistephus]* aster *m* de Chine
caltha *[Caltha]* caltha *m* des marais
calyx calice *m*
camellia *[Camellia]* camélia *m*;

camellia *m*

camomile; chamomile *[Anthemis]* camomille *f*

campanula *[Campanula]* campanule *f*; violette *f* de Marie; campanule *f* à feuilles rondes

canary creeper *[Tropaeolum canariensis]* capucine *f* de canaris

Canary Island ivy *[Hedera canariensis]* lierre *m* de canaris

candytuft; iberis *[Iberis]* thlaspi *m*; ibéride *f*; ibéris *m*

canker chancre *m*

canna *[Canna]* canna *m*; balisier *m*

Canterbury bell *[Campanula]* campanule *f* (à grosses fleurs); violette *f* de Marie

Canterbury hoe croc *m* à pommes de terre

Cape fuchsia *[Phygelius]* fuchsia *m* du Cap

Cape jasmin jasmin *m* du Cap

cape shamrock *[Oxalis]* oxalide *f*

capsicum *[Capsicum]* piment *m*

cardamine *[Cardamine]* cardamine *f* des prés

carline thistle *[Carlina]* carline *f*; carline vulgaire

carnation *[Dianthus]* œillet *m*

carpel carpelle *m*

carrot carotte *f*

carrot fly *[Psila rosae]* mouche *f* de la carotte

carthamus *[Carthamus]* carthame *m*

cash crop culture *f* de rapport; culture *f* commerciale

castor-oil plant *[Ricinus]* ricin *m*

catalpa *[Catalpa]* catalpe *f*; catalpa *m*

catchfly *[Silene]* silène *m*

catchweed, goose grass *[Galium]* gratteron *m*

caterpillar chenille *f*

catkin chaton *m*

catmint; *[Nepeta]* nepeta *f*

cat's tail; reed mace; bulrush massette *f*; quenouille *f*

cauliflower *[Brassica]* chou-fleur *m*

ceanothus *[Ceanothus]* céanothe *m*; céanote *m*

cedar; cedrus *[Cedrus]* cèdre *m*

cedar of Lebanon *[Cedrus libani]* cèdre *m* de Liban

celandine, greater *[Chelidonium majus]* chélidoine *f*; grande éclaire *f*

celandine, lesser *[Ranunculus ficaria]* ficaire *f*; petite éclaire *f*

celeriac céleri-rave *m*

celery céleri *m*

celosia *[Celosia]* célosie *f*

centaurea *[Centaurea]* centaurée *f* musquée; bleuet *m*

centaury *[Erythraea]* centaurée *f*

centaury, common *[Erythraea]* herbe *f* à mille florins

centipede scolopendre *f*; mille-pattes *m, inv*; mille-pieds *m, inv*

cerastium *[Cerastium]* céraiste *m*

cereus, torch thistle *[Cereus]* cierge *m*

cerinthe *[Cerinthe]* mélinet *m*

chainsaw scie *f* à chaine

chainsaw (electric) tronçonneuse *f* electrique

chainsaw (petrol engine) tronçonneuse *f* thermique

chalk craie *f*

chalk plant *[Gypsophila]* gypsophile *f*

chalky soil sol *m* crayeux; terre *f* calcaire

chamomile *[Anthemis]* anthémis *f* des teinturiers; œil-de-bœuf *m*

chard bette *f*

chaste tree; vitex *[Vitex]* vitex *m*

cheiranthus *[Cheiranthus]* giroflée *f* jaune; giroflée *f* des murailles

chelidonium *[Chelidonium]* chélidoine *f*

chemical fertilizer engrais *m* chimique

cherry cerise *f*

cherry (black) tree *[Prunus serotina]* cerisier *m*

cherry blossom fleurs *fpl* de cerisier

cherry laurel *[Prunus]* laurier-cerise *m*

cherry orchard cerisaie *f*

cherry-pie *[Heliotropium]* héliotrope *m* du Perou

cherry plum *[Prunus cerasifera]* prunier *m* cérasifère; myrobolan *m*

cherry tomato tomate *f* cerise

cherry tree *[Prunus avium]* cerisier *m*

chervil *[Anthricus]* cerfeuil *m*

chestnut marron *m*; châtaigne *f*
chestnut tree; horse chestnut tree
  [Aesculus] marronnier *m* d'Inde
chestnut tree, Spanish chestnut tree,
  sweet chestnut tree *[Castanea
  sativa]* châtaignier *m*; châtaignier *m*
  commun; marronnier *m*
chickweed *[Cerastium]* céraiste *m*
chicory endive *f*
China aster *[Callistephus]*
  reine-marguerite *f*
China rose *[Rosa]* rose *f* des quatre
  saisons
Chinese angelica tree; aralia *[Aralia]*
  angélique *f* de Chine
Chinese aster *[Callistephus]* aster *m* de
  Chine
Chinese azalea *[Azalea mollis]* azalée *f*
  de Chine
Chinese bellflower *[Platycodon]*
  platycodon
Chinese cabbage chou *m* de Chine
Chinese lantern; winter cherry
  [Physalis alkekengi] coqueret *m*; amour-
  en-cage *m*
Chinese pink *[Dianthus]* œillet *m* de
  chine
Chinese winter sweet; chimonanthus
  [Chimonanthus] chimonanthe
chionodoxa *[Chionodoxa]* gloire *f* de
  neige
chive *[Allium]* cive *f*; ciboule *f*; ciboulette
  f, civette *f*, brelette *f*
chlorosis chlorose *f*
Christmas rose *[Helleborus]* rose *f* de
  Noël; ellébore *m* noire; hellébore *m*
chrysalis chrysalide *f*
chrysanthemum *[Chrysanthemum]*
  chrysanthème *m*
chrysoplenium *[Chrysoplenium]*
  saxifrage *f* dorée
cineraria *[Cineraria]* cinéraire *f*
cinquefoil; potentilla *[Potentilla]*
  potentille *f*
citriculture culture *f* des agrumes
citrus fruit agrume *m*
clamp of potatoes silo *m* de pommes de
  terre
clarkia *[Clarkia]* clarkie *f*, clarkia *m*

clary *[Salvia sclarea]* sclarée *f*; sauge *f*
  sclarée
claw (to); rake (to) (soil); scratch (to)
  (brambles) griffer *v*
claw cultivator griffe-bineuse *f*
claw rake griffe *f*
clay terre *f* glaise; glaise *f*
clay soil; argillaceous soil terre *f*
  argileuse; terre limoueuse
clayey soil sol *m* argileux
clean (to); clear (to) nettoyer *v*
clear (to) (undergrowth or brushwood)
  débroussailler *v*
clear land (for cultivation) (to)
  défricher *v*
cleft graft greffe *f* en fente
cleft grafting; wedge grafting greffage
  m en fente
clematis *[Clematis]* clématite *f*; clématite
  f des haies
click beetle taupin *m*
climbing grimpant *adj*
climbing nasturtium *[Tropaeolum majus]*
  capucine *f* grimpante
climbing plant plante *f* grimpante
climbing rose rosier *m* grimpant
clippings (tree, hedge) branches *fpl*
  coupées
cloche cloche *f*
clod (of earth) motte *f* (de terre)
clove of garlic gousse *f* d'ail
cloud grass *[Agrostis]* agrostide *f*,
  agrostis *m*
clover trèfle *m*
club rush *[Scirpus]* scirpe *m*
clubroot (cabbage) hernie *f* du chou;
  gros-pied *m*
clump of flowers massif *m* de fleurs
cockchafer grub ver *m* blanc
cockchafer larva larve *f* du hanneton
cockchafer; maybug hanneton *m*
cockroach cafard *m*
codling moth pyrale *f* des pommes;
  carpocapse *f* des pommes
Colarado beetle doryphore *m*
colchicum *[Colchicum]* colchique *m*
  automnal; colchique *m* d'automne
coleus *[Coleus]* coléus *m*; coliole *f*
colocynth *[Cucurbita]* coloquinte *f*

colour couleur *f*; coloris *m*
coltsfoot *[Tussilago]* tussilage *m*; pas-d'âne *m*
columbine *[Aquilegia]* aquilegia *f*, aquilégie *f*; ancolie *f*
colutea *[Colutea]* baguenaudier *m*
combined hoe and fork serfouette *f*
come into bloom (to); come into blossom (to); blossom (to) s'épanouir *v*; fleurir *v*
comfrey *[Symphytum]* consoude *f*
commercial fruit growing culture *f* fruitière commerciale
commercial horticulture horticulture *f* commerciale
commercial vegetable growing culture *f* maraîchère commerciale
common centaury; erythraea *[Erythraea]* herbe *f* à mille florins
common maple *[Acer]* érable *m* champêtre
common red spider mite acarien *m* jaune commun (des serres)
compost compost *m*; terreau *m* de feuilles
compost (to) composter *v*
composting terrautage *m*
cornus *[Cornus]* cornouiller *m*
cone (eg of pine) cône *m*; pomme *f*
cone flower *[Rudbeckia]* rudbeckie *f*
conifer résineux *m, inv*
conifers conifères *mpl*
consound; symphytum *[Symphytum]* consoude *f*
container (eg plastic pot, etc) bac *m*; conteneur *m*
convolvulus; morning glory *[Ipomaea]* volubilis *m*
convolvulus; bindweed *[Convolvulus]* liseron *m*; liset *m*; liseron des champs
copper cuivre *m*; cuivre rouge
copper sulphate; copper sulfate sulfate *m* de cuivre
coppice; copse taillis *m*
coralwort *[Dentaria]* dentaire *f* à neuf feuilles
cordon (tree) cordon *m*
core (eg of apple) trognon *m*
coreopsis *[Coreopsis]* coréopsis *m*

coriander *[Coriandrum sativum]* coriandre *f*
corm bulbe *m*
corn crowfoot; ranunculus *[Ranunculus]* renoncule *f* des champs
corn flag; sword grass; sword lily *[Gladiolus]* glaïeul *m*
corn marigold; yellow marigold *[Chrysanthemum segetum]* marguerite *f* dorée
corn poppy *[Papaver]* coquelicot *m*
corn rocket *[Bunias erucago]* roquette *f* des champs
Cornelian cherry *[Cornus]* cornouiller *m*
cornflower *[Centaurea]* barbeau *m*; bleuet *m*; centaurée *f* bleuet; aubifoin *m*
cortaderia *[Cortaderia]* herbe *f* des pampas
corydalis *[Corydalis]* corydale *m*
corylopsis *[Corylopsis]* corylopsis
cos lettuce romaine *f*
cosmos *[Cosmos]* cosmos *m*
cotoneaster *[Cotoneaster]* cotonéastre *m*
cotton grass; eriophorum *[Eriophorum]* linaigrette *f*; jonc *m* à coton
couch grass chiendent *m* (officinal)
courgette courgette *f*
cow parsnip *[Heracleum]* berce *f* géante du Caucase
cowslip *[Primula veris]* primevère *f* commune; primevère *f* des champs; coucou *m*
crab apple pomme *f* sauvage
crab apple tree, wild crab apple tree *[Malus sylvestris]* pommier *m* sauvage
cranberry canneberge *f*
cranefly tipule *f*
cranesbill; pelargonium *[Pelargonium]* géranium *m*
creeper plante *f* grimpante; plante *f* rampante
crepis *[Crepis]* crépis *m*, crépide *f*
cress; garden cress cresson *m*; cresson *m* alénois
crinodendron *[Elaeocarpaceae]* crinodendron *m*
crocus *[Crocus]* crocus *m*; safran *m*
crocus, autumn flowering *[Crocus]*

safran *m* cultivé; safran *m* officinal
crop (of fruit etc) récolte *f*
crop growing; cropping culture *f*
crop that enriches the soil recolte *f* améliorante
cross-fertilize (to) (plants) faire *v* un croisement de
crown graft greffe *f* en couronne
crown grafting; bark grafting greffage en couronne
crown imperial *[Fritillaria]* couronne *f* impériale
crumble (to) émietter *v*
crumbling émiettage *m*
cuckoo flower *[Cardamine]* cardamine *f* des prés
cuckoo pint; lords and ladies *[Arum]* arum *m*; pied-de-veau *m*; gouet *m* d'Italie
cuckoo spit crachat *m* de coucou
cucumber concombre *m*
cultivar cultivar *m*; variété *f* cultivée
cultivar (for grafting) franc *m*; arbre *m* franc
cultivate cultiver *v*
cultivation culture *f*
cultivator binot *m*; griffe *f*
cupressus *[Cupressus]* cyprès *m*
curled endive chicorée *f*
currant (red, white) *[Ribes]* groseille *f* à grappes
currant bush groseillier *m*
cut (to) couper *v*
cut (to) (by scything or mowing) faucher *v*
cut back (to) (shoots, branch etc) rabattre *v*; ravaler *v*
cut flower fleur *f* coupée
cut to ground level (to) couper *v* à ras du sol
cutting bouture *f*
cutting; reaping fauchage *m*
cutting back (shoots, branch) rabattage *m*
cutting back; lopping ravalement *m*
cutworm ver *m* des moissons
cyclamen *[Cyclamen]* cyclamen *m*
cypress *[Cupressus]* cyprès *m*
cypress, Lawson *[Chamaecyparis lawsonia]* cyprès *m* de Lawson

cypripedium *[Cypripedium]* labelle *m*
cytisus cytise *m*

D

daffodil *[Narcissus]* jonquille *f*; jeannette *f* jaune; fleur *f* de coucou; coucou *m*; narcisse *f* sauvage
daffodil (wild) *[Narcissus, pseudoNarcissus]* chaudron *m*
dahlia *[Dahlia]* dahlia *m*
daisy (cultivated) *[Bellis]* pâquerette *f*; marguerite *f*
daisy (lawn) *[Bellis]* pâquerette *f*; petite marguerite *f*
damask rose *[Rosa damascena]* rose *f* incarnate
dame's violet *[Hesperis]* julienne *f* des dames; cassolette *f*; damas *m*
damp off (to) (seedlings) périr *v* de moississure d'excès d'humidité
damselfly; dragonfly agrion *m*
damson prune *f* de Damas; damas *m*
damson tree prunier *m* de Damas
danae *[Danae]* laurier *m* d'Alexandrie
dandelion *[Taraxacum]* dent-de-lion *f*; pissenlit *m*
dane-flower *[Pulsatilla (anemone)]* coquelourde *f*
daphne *[Daphne]* daphné *m*
day lily *[Hemerocallis]* hémérocalle *f*; hémérocallis *m*
dead bloom fleur *f* fanée
dead-nettle; archangel; White Nancy *[Lamium maculatum]* lamier *m* tacheté; lamier 'White Nancy' *m*
deadly nightshade *[Atropa belladonna]* belladone *f*
decay pourrissement *m*; pourriture *f*
decaying dépérissement *m*
deciduous caduc, caduque *adj*
deciduous leaves feuilles *fpl* caduques
deciduous tree arbre *m* à feuilles caduques
deciduous trees feuillus (les) *mpl*
deflower (to) défleurir *v*

delphinium *[Delphinium]* delphinium *m*; pied-d'alouette *m*

depth profondeur *f*

deutzia *[Deutzia]* deutzia

dewberry *[Rubus caesius]* ronce *f* bleu

dianthus (carnations, pinks, etc) *[Dianthus]* dianthus *m*; œillet *m* barbu; œillet *m* de poète

dibber; dibble plantoir *m*

dicentra *[Dicentra]* cœur-de-Marie *m*

dig (to) bêcher *v*

dig up (to) (a plant) déraciner *v*

digger piocheuse *f*

digging bêchage *m*

dill *[Anethum]* aneth *m*, aneth odorant; fenouil *m* bâtard; faux-fenouil *m*

disbud (to) escionner *v*; ébourgeonner *v*

disbudding escionnnement *m*; ébourgeonnement *m*; ébourgeonnage *m*

distribution of vegetable mould to ground terreautage *m*

ditch fossé *m*

ditch (open, between fields) douve *f*

ditch, drainage saignée *f*

divide (to); separate out (to); fork (to) (tree trunk) diviser *v*

dock *[Rumex]* oseille *f*

dog rose *[Rosa canina]* rose *f* de chien; églantine *f*

dog rose bush églantier *m*

dog's tooth violet *[Erythronium]* dent-de-chien *f*; érythrone *m*

dogwood tree *[Cornus]* cornouiller *m* sanguin

dogwood *[Cornus]* cornouiller *m*

doradilla; asplenium *[Asplenium]* doradille *f*

dormant dormant *adj*

double peony *[Paeonia]* rose *f* pivoine

double-headed hoe bêchard *m*

dragon (blood) tree; dracaena *[Dracaena]* dracéna *m*; dragonnier *m*

dragon's head *[Dracocephalum]* tête *f* de dragon

dragonfly libellule *f*

drain (to) drainer *v*; dessécher *v*; se dessécher *v*

drainage ditch saignée *f*

drainage; draining drainage *m*

draining spade louchet *m*

draw hoe binette *f*

drill plough sillonneur *m*

drosera *[Drosera]* drosère *f*, droséra *f*

drought; dryness sécheresse *f*

dry desséché,-e *adj*

dry rot carie *f*; le champignon; champignon *m* du bois; pourriture *f* sèche

dry rot fungus; merulius *[Merulius lacrymans]* mérule *m*

duster (for insecticides) poudreuse *f*

dusty miller; lychnis *[Lychnis coronaria]* coquelourde *f* des jardins

Dutch barn; open-sided barn hangar à recoltes

Dutch hoe ratissoire *f*

dwarf nain,-e *adj*

dwarf iris *[Iris pumila]* iris *m* nain

dwarf nasturtium *[Tropaeolum]* capucine *f* naine

dwarf rose rosier *m* nain; rosier miniature

dyer's greenweed *[Genista tinctoria]* herbe-à-jaunir *f*

dyer's rocket; weld *[Reseda luteola]* herbe-à-jaunir *f*

E

early (eg potato) précoce *adj*

early cultivation culture *f* hâtée

early crop culture *f* hâtée

early fruit; early vegetable hâtiveau *m*

earth; soil sol *m*; terre *f*; terroir *m*

earth up (to) terrer *v*

earthworm lombric *m*; ver *m* de terre

earwig perce-oreille *m*; forficule *f*

echeveria *[Echeveria]* écheveria *m*

echinops *[Echinops]* chardon *m* bleu

echium *[Echium]* herbe *f* aux vipères

edelweiss *[Leontopodium]* edelweiss *m* (des Alpes)

edger; edge cutter; powered edger taille-bordures *m*; coupe-bordures *m*

eelworm anguillule *f*; nématode *m*

efflorescence floraison *f*

eggplant *[Aubergine]* aubergine *f*
Egyptian lotus *[Nelumbium]* lotus *m*
elder *[Sambucus]* sureau *m*
elder, common *[Sambucus nigra]*
  sureau *m* noir
electric mower tondeuse *f* électrique
elm (young) ormeau *m*
elm, Dutch *[Ulmus x hollandica]* orme *m*
  hollandais
elm, English *[Ulmus campestris]* *[Ulmus*
  procera] orme *m* d'angleterre; orme
  champêtre
elm, wych; elm, Scotch [Ulmus glabra]
  orme *m* blanc; orme *m* de montagne
elsholtzia *[Elsholtzia]* elsholtzia *m*
endive endive *f*
enrich (to) enrichir *v*
epilobium *[Epilobium]* épilobe *m*; épilobe
  m à épi
epimedium *[Epimedium]* épimède *f*
equipment outillage *m*
eradicate (to); root out (to); pull out (to)
  (weeds) extirper *v*
erigeron *[Erigeron]* pulicaire *f*;
  érigéron *m*
erinus *[Erinus]* érine *f* des Alpes
erythronium *[Erythronium]* érythrone *m*;
  dent-de-chien *f*
eschscholtzia *[Eschscholtzia]*
  eschscholtzie *f*
espalier espalier *m*
eucalyptus eucalyptus *m*
eulalia *[Miscanthus]* eulalia *m*;
  miscanthe *m*
eupatorium *[Eupatorium]* eupatoire *f* à
  feuilles de chanvre
euphorbia *[Euphorbia]* poinsettie *f*;
  cierge *m*
European walnut noyer *m* d'Europe
evening primrose *[Oenothera]*
  œnothère *m*; onagre *f*; onagraire *f*
evergreen (tree) arbre *m* à feuilles
  persistantes; arbre *m* vert
evergreen thorn; fire-thorn
  [Pyracantha] buisson *m* ardente
everlasting flowers; helichrysum
  [Helichrysum] immortelles *fpl*
everlasting pea pois *m* vivace; gesse *f*
exochorda *[Exochorda]* exochorda

F

fair-maids-of-France; fair-maids-of-
  Kent *[Ranunculus]* renoncule *f* à feuilles
  d'aconit
fairy rose *[Rosa]* rose *f* pompon
false acacia *[Robinia]* faux acacia *m*;
  robinier *m*
false dittany *[Dictamnus]* fraxinelle *f*
false hellebore; white hellebore
  [Veratrum] vératre *m*; ellébore *m* blanc
feather grass *[Pennisetum]*
  pennisetum *m*
fence; fencing clôture *f*
fennel fenouil *m*
fern fougère *f*
fertilization fertilisation *f*
fertilizer engrais *m*
fertilizer spreader épandeur *m* à engrais
fertilizing fertilisation *f*
fescue grass *[Festuca]* fétuque *f*
feverfew *[Chrysanthemum parthenium]*
  matricaire *f*
field maple *[Acer]* érable *m* champêtre
field mouse mulot *m*
field-vole campagnol *m*
fig figue *f*
fig tree *[Ficus carica]* figuier *m*
fir *[Abies]* sapin *m*
fir, Douglas; Oregon pine *[Pseudotsuga*
  menziesii] Douglas vert; sapin *m* de
  Douglas; sapin *m* de l'Oregon
firethorn *[Pyracantha]* buisson *m*
  ardente
fishbone thistle *[Cirsium; Cnicus]* cirse
  m; cirsium *m*
flagstone dalle *f*
flame nettle *[Coleus]* coléus *m*; coliole *f*
flax; linum *[Linum]* lin *m*
fleabane; erigeron *[Erigeron]* érigéron
  m; pulicaire *f*; vergerette *f*
floral floral,-e *adj*
floribunda rose bush rosier *m* floribunda
florist fleuriste *m,f*; boutique *f* de fleuriste
floss flower *[Ageratum]* agérate *m*;
  ageratum *m*
flower fleur *f*

flower again (to) (in same year) surfleurir *v*

flower arrangement composition *f* florale; art *m* de faire des bouquets

flower bed parterre *m*; plate-bande *f*; planche *f*

flower bed, round corbeille *f*

flower bulb bulbe *m* à fleur

flower garden jardin *m* d'agrément; parc *m* floral

flower grower jardinier-fleuriste *m*

flower head capitule *m*

flower shop fleuriste *m,f*; boutique *f* de fleuriste

flower show exposition *f* de fleurs; exposition florale; floralies *fpl*

flower stand; window box jardinière *f*

flowering cherry; prunus *[Prunus]* cerisier *m* à fleurs

flowering crab apple tree; malus *[Malus]* pommier *m* à fleurs

flowering crab; Japanese crab *[Malus floribunda]* pommier-cerise *m*

flowering currant *[Ribes sanguineum]* groseillier *m* à fleurs

flowering plant plante *f* à fleurs

flowering plum; prunus *[Prunus]* prunier *m* à fleurs

flowering rush; butomus *[Butomus]* jonc *m* fleuri

flowering shrub arbuste *m* à fleurs

flowerpot pot *m* à fleurs

fly honeysuckle *[Lonicera]* chèvrefeuille *m* des buissons

foam flower; tiarella *[Tiarella]* tiarella *m*

foliation feuillaison *f*; foliation *f*

force (to) hâter *v*; forcer *v*

forcing forçage *m*

forget-me-not, myosotis *[Myosotis sylvatica]* ne m'oubliez pas *m inv*; oreille-de-souris *f*; myosotis *m*; myosotis *m* des marais

fork; garden fork fourche *f* à bêcher

formation of tubers tubérisation *f*

forsythia *[Forsythia]* forsythia *m*

four-tined clawing hook croc *m* à griffer

fox renard *m*

fox tail; eremurus *[Eremurus]* quenouille *f* de Cléopâtre

foxglove *[Digitalis]* digitale *f* (pourprée); digitale pourpre

frame, cold couche *f* froide; châssis *m* froid

frame, Dutch; Dutch light châssis *m* hollandais

frame, forcing châssis *m* pour culture forcée

frame, glazed; glass frame châssis *m* vitré

frame, hot châssis *m* chaud

frame, temperate couche *f* tiède

fraxinella *[Dictamnus]* fraxinelle *f*

freesia *[Freesia]* freesia *m*

French bean haricot *m* vert

French honeysuckle *[Hedysarum]* sainfoin *m* d'Espagne; sainfoin *m* à bouquets

French marigold *[Tagetes]* œillet *m* d'Inde; petit œillet *m* d'Inde; tagète *m*

fritillary; fritillaria *[Frittillaria]* fritillaire *f*; fritillaire *f* méléagride; fritillaire *f* damier

fruit and vegetable growing culture *f* fruitière et maraîchère

fruit crop; fruit cropping cueillette *f* des fruits

fruit crops cultures *fpl* fruitières

fruit farming culture *f* fruitière

fruit grower; fruit farmer producteur *m* de fruits

fruit shrub arbuste *m* fruitier

fruit tree arbre *m* fruitier

fuchsia *[Fuchsia]* fuchsia *m*; fuchsia *m* de pleine terre

fumigate (to) fumiger *v*

fumigation fumigation *f*

fumitory *[Corydalis]* corydale *m*

fungicide fongicide *m*

fungus champignon *m*

furse; gorse *[Ulex europaeus]* ajonc *m*; ajonc d'Europe

G

galega *[Galega]* galéga *m*

gaillardia *[Gaillardia]* gaillarde *f*

garden jardin *m*
garden (to); do gardening (to) jardiner *v*; faire *v* du jardinage
garden centre pépinière *f*, garden-centre *m*
garden cress cresson *m* alénois
garden fork fourche-beche *f*
garden mould terre *f* franche; terreau *m*
garden path allée *f*
garden rocket *[Hesperis]* cassolette *f*
garden rocket *[Eruca sativa]* roquette *f*
garden rubbish détritus *mpl* de jardin; déchets *mpl* du jardin
garden seat banc *m* de jardin
garden shed abri *m* de jardin; remise *f*
garden shoes sabots *mpl* de jardin
garden soil terre *f* émiettée
garden sorrel *[Rumex]* oseille *f*
garden trowel transplantoir *m*; déplantoir *m*
garden waste; garden refuse déchets *mpl* du jardin
garden(ing) tools outils *mpl* de jardinage
gardener's garters *[Phalaris]* ruban *m* de bergère
gardener's line cordeau *m* de jardinier
gardenia *[Gardenia]* gardénia *m*; gardénie *f*
gardening jardinage *m*
garland flower; daphne *[Daphne]* bois-joli *m*; daphné *m*
garlic ail *m*
gate portillon *m*
gather in the harvest (to) rentrer *v* la recolte
gaultheria *[Gaultheria]* gaulthérie *f*
gaura *[Gaura]* gaura
gauze flower *[Gypsophila]* gypsophile *f*
gean; wild cherry; mazzard; bird cherry *[Prunus avium]* merisier *m*; merisier *m* des oiseaux
genista *[Genista]* genêt *m* d'Espagne
gentian *[Gentiana]* gentiane *f*
geranium *[Pelargonium]* géranium *m*; géranium des fleuristes; géranium des jardins; pélargonium *m*
germander; teucrium *[Teucrium]* germandrée *f*
giant bell-flower *[Campanula]*
campanule *f* (à grosses fleurs)
gingko *[Ginkgo biloba]* arbre *m* aux quarante écus
give the soil a dressing (to) donner *v* une façon à la terre
gladiolus *[Gladiolus]* glaïeul *m*
glasshouse serre *f*
globe flower; trollius *[Trollius]* trolle *m*; boule-d'or *f*
globe thistle *[Echinops]* chardon *m* bleu
glory lily; gloriosa *[Gloriosa]* méthonique *f*
glory-of-the-snow *[Chionodoxa]* gloire *f* de neige
gloxinia *[Gloxinia]* gloxinie *f*
goat's beard *[Aruncus]* barbe-de-bouc *f*
goat's rue *[Galega]* galéga *m*
godetia *[Godetia]* godétia *f*, godétie *f*
godetia; evening primrose *[Oenethera]* œenethère *m*
gold dust; golden tuft; *[Alyssum]* corbeille *f* d'or
golden rod; solidago *[Solidago]* verge *f* d'or; solidage *f*
golden saxifrage *[Chrysoplenium]* saxifrage *f* dorée
gombo; ladies fingers gombo *m*
goose grass *[Galium]* gratteron *m*
gooseberry *[Ribes]* groseille *f* à maquereau; groseille *f* verte
gooseberry bush groseillier *m* à maquereau
gourd courge *f*; gourde *f*
graft greffe *f*; greffon *m*; ente *f*
graft (to) (tree) greffer *v*
graft onto a cultivar (to) greffer *v* sur franc
grafting greffage *m*
grafting knife greffoir *m*
grafting wax; tree grafting wax mastic *m* à greffer
grafting, double; double grafting; intergrafting double greffage *m*
grafting, root greffage *m* sur racine
grafting, splice; whip grafting greffage *m* à l'anglaise simple
grafting, tongue greffage *m* à l'anglaise compliqué
grape raisin *m*; grain *m* de raisin

grape harvest vendange *f*
grape hyacinth *[Muscari]* muscari *m*
grape mealy bug cochenille *f* de la vigne
grapefruit *[Citrus grandis]*
  pamplemousse *m*
grass herbe *f*
grass border; border plate-bande *f*
grass plot parterre *m* de gazon
grass over (to) (garden) gazonner *v*
grass over (to) (land,field) enherber *v*;
  couvrir *v* d'herbe
grass shears cisaille *f* à gazon
grass snake couleuvre *f*
grasses graminées *fpl*
great reed; arundo *[Arundo]* canne *f* de
  Provence
Greek mallow *[Sidalcea]* sidalcée *f*;
  sidalcea *m*
Greek Valerian *[Polemonium]* valériane
  f grecque bleue
green cabbage chou *m* pommé vert
green fingers main *f* vert
green lace-wing chrysope *f*
greenfly puceron *m* (des plantes);
  puceron *m* vert; aphis *m*; aphidés *mpl*;
  aphidiens *mpl*
greengage reine-claude *f*
greenhouse serre *f*
greenhouse plant; glasshouse plant
  plante *f* de serre
greenhouse, unheated; cold house
  serre *f* froide
grey mould pourriture *f* grise
ground terre *f*; terroir *m*
ground cherry *[Physalis]* coqueret *m*
ground limestone calcaire *m* broyé
groundsel *[Senecio]* séneçon *m*;
  cinéraire *f* maritime
grow (to) pousser *v*
grub out stumps (to) essoucher *v*
grubber arracheuse *f*
grubbing out stumps; uprooting
  essouchage *m*
grubbing hook croc *m* à défricher
guelder rose *[Viburnum]* boule-de-
  neige *f*
Guernsey lily *[Nerine sarniensis]* lis *m*
  de Japon
gypsophila *[Gypsophila]* gypsophile *f*

H

hair grass; panicum *[Panicum]* panic *m*
  effilé
half standard demi-tige *m*; arbre *m* en
  demi-tige
half-standard rose rosier *m* demi-tige
hamamelis *[Hamamelis]* hamamélis *m*
hand fork fourche *f* à fleurs
hand mower tondeuse *f* mécanique
hand saw (small) égoïne *f*
hand seeder semoir *m* à main
hanging basket corbeille *f* suspendue
hardy (plant) rustique *adj*; résistant *adj*
  au gel; vivace *adj*
hardy annual plante *f* annuelle résistante
  au gel
hardy perennial plante *f* vivace
hare lièvre *m*
hare's ear *[Bupleurum]* oreille-de-lièvre *f*;
  buplèvre *m*
harebell *[Campanula]* campanule *f* à
  feuilles rondes
haricot bean haricot *m*; phaséole *f*;
  soissons *m*
harrow herse *f*
hart's tongue fern; phyllitis *[Phyllitis]*
  langue-de-cerf *f*
harvest récolte *f*
hatchet hachette *f*
haulm (of potatoes etc) fane *f*
haw cenelle *f*
hawksbeard *[Crepis]* crépis *m*, crépide *f*
hawkweed *[Hieracium]* épervière *f*
hawthorn *[Crataegus]* aubépine *f*, épine
  f blanche
hazel tree; corylus; cobnut (tree)
  [Corylus avellana] noisetier *m*;
  coudrier *m*
hazelnut noisette *f*
heath; heather; heathland brande *f*
heath soil; heather soil; heath mould
  terre *f* de bruyère
heather; heathland bruyère *f*
hedge; hedgerow haie *f*

hedge clipper cisaille *f* à haie
hedgecutter taille-haies *m*
hedge nettle; stachys *[Stachys]* épiaire *f*; stachyde *f*
hedge shears cisailles *fpl* à haies
hedgehog hérisson *m*
hedgetrimmer; taille-haies *m*
helianthemum *[Helianthemum]* hélianthème *m*
helichrysum *[Helichrysum]* immortelles *fpl*
heliotrope *[Heliotropium]* héliotrope *m*; héliotrope *m* du Perou
helleborine *[Serapias]* helléborine *f*
helleborus *[Helleborus]* ellébore *m* noire; hellébore *m*
hemerocallis *[Hemerocallis]* hémérocalle *f*; hémérocallis *m*
hemp agrimony *[Eupatorium]* eupatoire *f* à feuilles de chanvre
heracleum *[Heracleum]* berce *f* géante du Caucase
herb herbe *f*
herb garden jardin *m* d'herbes aromatiques
herb Paris; true love (herb) *[Paris quadrifolia]* parisette *f* à quatre feuilles
herbaceous herbacé *adj*
herbicidal herbicide *adj*
herbicide désherbant *m*; herbicide *m*
hesperis *[Hesperis]* julienne *f* des dames
heuchera *[Heuchera]* heuchère *f*
hibiscus *[Hibiscus]* hibiscus *m*
hickory *[Carya]* hickory *m*; noyer *m* d'Amérique
hieracium *[Hieracium]* épervière *f*
hip fruit *m* d'églantier
hoe houe *f*; binette *f*; binot *m*
hoe, Dutch binette *f* à pousser
hoe, two-pronged binoche *f*
hoe (to) biner *v* (le sol); houer *v*; binocher *v*; ratisser *v* (une allée); serfouir *v*
hoe (to) (vegetables) serfouir *v* (les plantes potagères)
hoe (to) (weeds) sarcler *v* (les mauvaises herbes)
hoeing binage *m* (du sol); serfouage *m*; houement *m*; serfouissage *m*

hoeing (weeds) sarclage *m* (de mauvaises herbes)
holly; ilex *[Ilex aquifolium]* houx *m* commun
hollyhock *[Althaea rosea]* passe-rose *f*; rose *f* trémière
holm oak *[Quercus ilex]* chêne *m* vert
honest *[Lunaria]* satin *m* blanc
honesty *[Lunaria]* monnaie-du-pape *f*; lunaire *f*
honeysuckle *[Lonicera]* chèvrefeuille *m*
honeysuckle, winter *[Lonicera fragantissima]* chèvrefeuille *m* d'hiver
honeysuckle, fly *[Lonicera]* chèvrefeuille *m* des buissons
honeysuckle, French *[Hedysarum]* sainfoin *m* à bouquets; sainfoin *m* d'Espagne
honeywort *[Cerinthe]* cérinthe *m*; mélinet *m*
hop; humulus *[Humulus]* houblon *m*
hop (Japanese) houblon *m* de Japon
hormone rooting powder hormones *fpl* de bouturage
hornbeam *[Carpinus betulus]* charme *m*; faux bouleau *m*
hornbeam; hornbeam hedgerow *[Carpinus]* charmille *f*
horse chestnut tree *[Aesculus hippocastanum]* marronnier *m* d'Inde
horse manure fumier *m* de cheval
horse mint; monarda *[Monarda]* monarde *f*
horseradish *[Cochlearia armoracia]* *[Armoracia rusticana]* raifort *m*; radis *m* à cheval; moutarde *f* des Capucins; rave *f* de campagne
horsetail; equisetum *[Equisetum]* prêle *f*; prêle *f*
horticultural compost terreau *m* horticole
horticulture horticulture *f*
hose; garden hose tuyau *m* d'arrosage
hose reel dévidoir *m*
hotbed couche *f* chaude
hothouse plant plante *f* de serre
house plant plante *f* d'appartement; plante *f* verte
household garden jardin *m* de rapport

houselee *[Sempervivum]* joubarbe *f*
houstonia *[Houstonia]* houstonia *f*
hover mower tondeuse *f* sur coussin d'air
humus humus *m*; terreau *m*
hyacinth *[Hyacinthus]* jacinthe *f*
hybrid hybride *adj & m*
hybrid plant plante *f* hybride
hybrid variety variété *f* hybride
hydrangea *[Hydrangea]* hortensia *m*
hydroponics culture *f* hydroponique; culture *f* sans sol

IJK

iberis *[Iberis]* ibéride *f*, ibéris *m*
ice plant *[Mesembryanthemum]* cristalline *f*
impatiens *[Impatiens glandulifera]* impatiente *f* glanduleuse
impatiens; balsamine; garden balsam; busy Lizzie *[Impatiens balsamina]* impatiens *f*; balsamine *f*
incarvillea *[Incarvillea]* incarvillée *f*
Indian bean tree; catalpa *[Catalpa]* catalpa *m*; catalpe *f*
Indian rose *[Rosa]* rose *f* des quatre saisons
indian shot *[Canna]* canna *m*; alisier *m*
indigo plant; indigofera *[Indigofera]* indigotier *m*; indigofera *m*
inorganic fertilizer engrais *m* minéral
insect bite or sting piqûre *f*
intergrafting surgreffage *m*
inula; fleabane; elecampane *[Inula]* inule *f*; inula *f*
ipomoea *[Ipomoea]* ipomée *f*; belle-de-jour *f*; volubilis *m*
iris; flag *[Iris]* iris *m* (des marais)
iris; garden iris; German iris *[Iris germanica]* iris *m* des jardins
irrigate (to) irriguer *v*
irrigation irrigation *f*
ivy *[Hedera]* lierre *m*
ivy geranium; ivy-leaved geranium *[Pelargonium]* géranium *m* lierre

jacaranda *[Jacaranda]* jacaranda *m*
Jacob's Ladder *[Polemonium]* valériane *f* grecque bleue
Japanese azalea *[Azalea japonica]* azalée *f* de Japon
Japanese maple *[Acer]* érable *m* du Japon
jasmine *[Jasminum]* jasmin *m*
Jerusalem artichoke *[Helianthus tuberosa]* topinambour *m*
Jerusalem sage; phlomis *[Phlomis]* phlomide *f*
Jew's mallow *[Kerria]* kerria *m*; kerrie *f*
Judas tree *[Cercis]* arbre *m* de Judée
juniper *[Juniperus]* genévrier *m*
Jupiter's beard *[Sempervivum]* joubarbe *f*
kale; curly kale chou *m* frisé
kalmia; mountain laurel *[Kalmia]* kalmie *f*
Kansas feather *[Liatris]* liatride *f*
kerria; Japanese rose *[Kerria]* kerria *m*; kerrie *f*
kidney bean haricot *m*; soissons *m*
kidney bean (small) flageolet *m*
kingcup *[Ranunculus]* bouton *m* d'or
king's spear *[Asphodeline]* bâton *m* royal; asphodèle *m* blanc
kitchen garden jardin *m* potager; potager *m*
kniphofia *[Kniphofia]* tritome *m*
knotgrass; knotweed *[Polygonum]* renouée *f*
kochia *[Kochia]* faux-conifère *m*

L

laburnum; golden rain tree *[Laburnum vulgare]* cytise *m* pluie d'or; cytise faux ébénier
ladder échelle *f*
ladies fingers; gombo gombo *m*
ladies mantle *[Alchemilla]* alchémille *f*
lady's slipper orchid *[Cypripedium]* sabot *m* de la Vierge; sabot de Vénus; labelle *m*

lady's smock *[Cardamine]* cardamine *f*
des prés
ladybird coccinelle *f*
lamb's skin *[Arnica]* arnica *f* des
montagnes; arnique *f* des montagnes
landscape paysage *m*
landscape gardener jardinier,-ière *m,f*
paysagiste; dessinateur,-trice *m,f* de
jardins paysagers
landscaping aménagements *mpl*
paysagers
lantana *[Lantana]* lantana *m*; lantanier *m*
larch, common; larch, European *[Larix
decidua]* mélèze *m*
larkspur; delphinium *[Delphinium]*
pied-d'alouette *m*
larva larve *f*
late (eg potato) tardif,-ive *adj*
late crop culture *f* retardée
laurel, common *[Prunus]* laurier-cerise *m*
lavender; lavandula *[Lavandula]*
lavande *f*
lavender cotton *[Santolina]* santoline *f*;
aurone *f* femelle
lawn pelouse *f*, gazon *m*
lawn edger coupe-bordures *m*
lawn rake balai *m* à gazon; balai *m* à
feuilles
lawn shears cisaille *f* à gazon
lawn sweeper (machine) balayeuse *f* à
gazon
layer (to) marcotter *v*
layer; runner marcotte *f*
layering marcottage *m*
leadwort; plumbago *[Plumbago]*
dentelaire *f* d'Europe
leaf feuille *f*
leaf drop; leaf fall défeuillaison *f*;
défoliation *f*
leaf mould; terreau *m* de feuilles
leaf sweeper for lawns (machine)
balayeuse *f* à gazon
leafy; deciduous feuillu,-e *adj*
leatherjacket larve *f* de la tipule
leek poireau *m*
lemon citron *m*
lemon balm; melissa *[Melissa]* melisse
f citronnelle
lemon tree citronnier *m*

leontopodium *[Leontopodium]*
edelweiss *m* (des Alpes)
leopard plant *[Ligularia]* ligulaire *f*;
ligularia *m*
leopard's bane *[Doronicum]* doronic *m*;
doronic *m* du Caucase
lettuce laitue *f*
lettuce, cabbage laitue *f* pommée
lettuce, summer laitue *f* d'été
level out (to) (soil) égaliser *v*
liatris *[Liatris]* liatride *f*
lichen lichen *m*
lifter; grubber arracheuse *f*
light plough binot *m*
ligularia *[Ligularia]* ligulaire *f*; ligularia *m*
ligustrum *[Ligustrum]* troène *m*
lilac (bush, flower) *[Syringa]* lilas *m*
lily *[Lilium]* lis *m*; lys *m*
lily of the valley; convallaria
[Convallaria] muguet *m*; lis *m* des
vallées; lis *m* de mai
lily, tiger *[Lilium]* lis *m* tigré
lime (citrus) lime *f*; citron *m* vert
lime (mineral) chaux *f*
lime (slaked) chaux *f* éteinte
lime tree, sweet (citrus) *[Citrus limetta]*
limettier *m*
lime tree; linden tree; European lime
[Tilia x europaea] tilleul *m*
lime, large-leaved *[Tilia platyphyllos]*
tilleul *m* à grandes feuilles
lime, small-leaved *[Tilia cordata]* tilleul
m à petites feuilles
liming chaulage *m*
linden tree *[Tilia]* tilleul *m*
liverwort *[Hepatica]* trinitaire *f*
lizard lézard *m*
loamy sand sable *m* gras
lobelia *[Lobelia]* lobélie *f*
locust tree *[Robinia]* robinier *m*
loganberry loganberry *m*
London pride *[Saxifraga]* désespoir *m*
des peintres; saxifrage *f* ombreuse
long-lived vivace *adj*
long shoot rameau *m* à bois
loosen (to) or break up (to) the ground
ameublir *v* la terre; serfouir *v*
loosestrife *[Lysimachia]* lysimachie *f*;
lysimaque *f*

lop (to) ébrancher *v*
lopping; thinning ébranchage *m*;
émondage *m*; élagage *m*
lopping shears ébrancheur *m*
lords and ladies *[Arum]* gouet *m* d'Italie;
pied-de-veau *m*; arum *m* maculé
love-in-a-mist *[Nigella]* nigelle *f* de
Damas
love-lies-bleeding *[Amaranthus]*
queue-de-renard *f*; amarante *f* à fleurs
en queue
lunaria *[Lunaria]* monnaie-du-pape *f*
lungwort *[Pulmonaria]* pulmonaire *f*
officinale
lupin *[Lupinus]* lupin *m*
lupin, perennial *[Lupinus]* lupin *m* vivace
lychnis *[Lychnis]* lychnide *f*; lychnis *m*
lyre flower *[Dicentra]* cœur-de-
Jeannette *m*; cœur-de-Marie *m*
lythrum *[Lythrum]* salicaire *f* commune

M

Madagascar jasmine *[Stephanotis
floribunda]* jasmin *m* de Madagascar
Madonna lily *[Lilium]* lis *m* blanc
madwort *[Alyssum]* alysse *f*; alysson *m*;
corbeille *f* d'or
maggoty véreux *adj*
magnesian limestone chaux *f*
magnésienne
magnesium magnésium *m*
magnolia; magnolia tree *[Magnolia]*
magnolia *m*; magnolier *m*
mahonia 'Charity' *[Mahonia x 'Charity']*
mahonia *m* 'Charity'
maidenhair fern *[Adiantum]* adiante *m*;
capillaire *m*; cheveux *mpl* de Venus
maidenhair tree; ginkgo *[Ginkgo biloba]*
arbre *m* aux quarante écus
maize maïs *m*
mallow; lavatera *[Lavatera]* lavatère *f*;
lavatère *f* maritime
mallow; malva *[Malva]* mauve *f*
mandarin tree mandarinier *m*
mandevilla; Chile jasmine *[Mandevilla]*

jasmin *m* de Chili
manure fumier *m*; fumure *f*
manure spreader épandeur *m* de fumier
manuring fumure *f*
maple *[Acer]* érable *m*; érable *m*
champêtre
mare's tail; hippuris *[Hippuris]* pesse *f*
marguerite *[Chrysanthemum]*
marguerite *f*, grande
marigold *[Calendula]* souci *m*
**marigold; Scotch marigold; pot-
marigold** *[Calendula]* souci *m* des
jardins
maritime pine *[Pinus]* pin *m* maritime
maritime pine bark écorce *f* de pin
maritime
marjoram; sweet marjoram *[Origanum
majorana]* marjolaine *f*
market garden jardin *m* de rapport
market garden produce produits *mpl*
maraîchers
market gardener jardinier *m* maraîcher
market gardener; horticulturist
horticulteur *m*
marrow; vegetable marrow courge *f*;
courge *f* aubergine; courge *f* à la moelle
marsh marigold; caltha *[Caltha]* caltha
m des marais; bouton *m* d'or des marais
marshy marécageux,-euse *adj*
marvel of Peru; mirabilis *[Mirabilis]*
belle-de-nuit *f*
matthiola *[Matthiola]* matthiole *f*;
mathiole *f*
mattock hoyau *m*; pic *m* à tranche
mattock (point and hoe) pioche *f*
meadow mouse; field vole campagnol *m*
meadow rhubarb *[Thalictrum]* rue *f* des
prés; pigamon *m* des prés
meadow rue; thalictrum *[Thalictrum]*
rue *f* des prés; pigamon *m*; pigamon *m*
des prés
meadow saffron; autumn crocus
[Colchicum autumnale] veilleuse *f*;
tue-chien *m, inv*; colchique *m* automnal;
colchique *m* d'automne
meadow sage sauge *f* sauvage; sauge *f*
des prés
meal moth pyrale *f*
mealy bug cochenille *f* des serres;

51

mullein

pseudococcus *m*
medicinal herbs herbes *fpl* médicinales
medlar; mespilus *[Mespilus germanica]*
néflier *m*
melilot *[Melilotus]* mélilot
melissa; balm *[Melittis]* mélisse *f*
officinale
melittis *[Melittis]* mélitte *f*, mélisse *f*
sauvage
mellow the soil (to) ameublir *v* la terre
mesembryanthemum *[Mesembryanthe-
mum]* mésembryanthéme *m*; cristalline *f*
Mexican ivy *[Cobaea]* cobée *f*, cobea *m*
Mexican lily lis *m* du Mexique
Mexican orange; choisya *[Choisya]*
oranger *m* du Mexique
Mexican sunflower *[Tithonia]* tithonia
Michaelmas daisy *[Aster]* marguerite *f*
de la Saint-Michel; marguerite *f*
d'automne; aster *m* d'automne
mignonette *[Reseda]* réséda *m* odorant;
mignonnette *f*
mildew mildiou *m*
mildewed; mildewy mildiousé,-e *adj*
milfoil *[Achillea]* achillée *f*
milkweed; asclepias *[Asclepias]*
herbe-aux-perruches *f*
milkwort *[Polygala]* herbe *f* au lait;
polygale *m* commun
millet millet *m*
millipede mille-pattes *m, inv*; mille-pieds
m, inv
mimosa *[Mimosa]* mimosa *m*
mimulus *[Mimulus]* mimule *m*
mineral fertlizer engrais *m* minéral
mint *[Mentha]* menthe *f*
mistletoe; viscum *[Viscum]* gui *m*
mock orange *[Philadelphus]* seringa *m*;
seringat *m*
mole taupe *f*
molucca balm *[Molucella]* cloche *f*
d'Irlande
momordica *[Momordica]* momordique *f*
monkey flower *[Mimulus]* mimule *m*
monkey puzzle tree *[Araucaria]*
araucaria *m*
monkshood *[Aconitum napellus]* aconit
m; aconit *m* napel
montbretia; crocosmia *[Crocosmia;*

Crocosma] montbrétia *m*; montbrétie *f*
monthly rose *[Rosa]* rose *f* des quatre
saisons
moon-flower *[Ipomoea]* ipomée *f*
bonne-nuit
moonwort; lunaria *[Lunaria]* lunaire *f*
moonwort *[Soldanella]* soldanelle *f*
moorwort *[Andromeda]* andromède *f*
moorland lande *f*; bruyère *f*
morning glory *[Ipomoea]* belle-de-jour *f*,
ipomée *f*; volubilis *m*
moss mousse *f*
moss remover émousseur *m*
moss rose *[Rosa centifolia muscosa]*
rose *f* mousseuse
mossy saxifrage *[Saxifraga]* saxifrage *f*
mousseuse
motherwort *[Leonurus cardiaca]*
agripaume *f*
motor mower tondeuse *f* à moteur
mould moisissure *f*
mould (heath) terre *f* de bruyère
mould (vegetable); loam terreau *m*; terre
f végétale
mouldboard plough charrue *f* à soc
mountain ash; rowan *[Sorbus]* sorbier
m commun; sorbier des oiseleurs;
sorbier des oiseaux; cochène *m*
mountain avens *[Dryas]* dryade *f* à huit
pétales
mountain pine *[Pinus]* pin *m* de
montagne
mouse souris *f*
mouse-ear; chickweed *[Cerastium]*
céraiste *m*
mousetrap souricière *f*
mow (to) (lawn, grass) tondre *v*
mower; grass cutter tondeuse *f*,
tondeuse *f* à gazon
mowing tondaison *f*; tonte *f*
mowing (of hay) fauchage *m*
mud; silty limoneux,-euse *adj*
mulberry mûre *f*
mulberry tree mûrier *m*
mulch paillis *m*; couverture *f* d'humus
mulch (to) pailler *v*
mulching paillage *m*
mullein *[Verbascum]* molène *f*,
bouillon-blanc *m*; cierge *m*

musa *[Musa]* bananier *m* d'ornement
mushroom champignon *m*
musk rose rose *f* musquée
mustard moutarde *f* blanche
mustard and cress moutarde *f* blanche et cresson *m* alénois
mustard seed graine *f* de moutarde
myosotis *[Myosotis]* myosotis *m*; oreille-de-souris *f*; ne m'oubliez pas *m inv*
myriapod myriapode *m*
myrtle *[Myrtus]* myrte *m*

N

nandina [Nandina] nandina
Napier grass; pennisetum [Pennisetum] pennisetum
narcissus *[Narcissus]* narcisse *m*
nasturtium *[Tropaeolum]* capucine *f*
nasturtium, climbing *[Tropaeolum majus]* capucine *f* grimpante
nasturtium, dwarf *[Tropaeolum]* capucine *f* naine
navelwort *[Omphalodes]* ombilic *m*; gobelets *mpl*; nombril *m* de Venus
nectarine brugnon *m*; nectarine *f*
nectarine tree brugonier *m*
nemesia *[Nemesia]* némésia *m*
nerine *Nerine sarniensis]* lis *m* de Japon
nenuphar; water-lily *[Nuphur]* nénuphar *m*
nepenthes *[Nepenthes]* népenthe *m*; népenthés *m*
nepeta *[Nepeta]* nepeta *f*
net; netting (over fruit bushes, etc) filet *m*
nettle *[Urtica]* ortie *f*
nettle sting piqûre *f* d'ortie
New Zealand burr *[Acaena]* acaena *f*
nierembergia [Nierembergia] nierembergia
nigella *[Nigella]* nigelle *f* de Damas
nitrogen azote *m*
noble laurel; bay laurel;sweet bay *[Laurus nobilis]* laurier *m* commun; laurier noble; laurier d'Apollon; laurier-

sauce *m*
nodule nodule *m*
nopal *[Opuntia]* raquette *f*
Norway maple *[Acer]* érable *m* plane
notch grafting greffage *m* en incrustation
nursery pépinière *f*
nursery bed plate-bande *f* de pépinière
nurseryman pépiniériste *m*
nymphaea *[Nymphaea]* nymphéa *m*

O

oak; oak, English *[Quercus robur]* *[Quercus pedunculata]* chêne *m*; chêne pedonclé; chêne rouvre
oak, holm; oak, holly *[Quercus ilex]* chêne *m* vert
oak, sessile *[Quercus petraea]* *[Quercus sessiliflora]* chêne *m* à glands sessiles; chêne à fleurs sessiles
oak-leaf lettuce feuille *f* de chêne
oenothera; evening primrose *[Oenothera]* œnothère *m*
oidium oïdium *m*
okra; gombo; ladies fingers gombo *m*
oleander *[Nerium]* laurier-rose *m*; rose-laurier *m* (a)
oleaster *[Elaeagnus]* oléastre *m*; chalef *m*
olive olive *f*
olive grove olivette *f*; olivaie *f*; oliveraie *f*
olive tree *[Olea]* olivier *m*
olive-growing oléiculture *f*
olive-growing (land) oléicole *adj*
omphalodes *[Omphalodes]* ombilic *m*; nombril *m* de Venus
onion oignon *m*
onion leaf beetle crocère *m* de l'oignon
open hotbed; manure hotbed couche *f* à fumier
orache; atriplex *[Atriplex]* arroche *f*
orange blossom fleur *f* d'oranger
orange lily *[Lilium]* lis *m* orangé
orange tree *[Citrus]* oranger *m*
orchard verger *m*; jardin *m* fruitier
orchard area surface *f* plantée en vergers

orchid *[Orchid]* orchidée *f*, orchis *m*
orchid, military; soldier orchid orchis *m* militaire
orchid, purple orchis *m* pourpre
orchid, spotted *[Orchis maculata]* orchis *m* tacheté
ornamental banana plant *[Musa]* bananier *m* d'ornement
ornamental gourd *[Cucurbita]* citrouille *f*
ornamental lake; pond bassin *m*
ornamental pear; pyrus *[Pyrus]* poirier *m* d'ornement
ornamental plant plante *f* d'ornement
ornamental shrub arbuste *m* d'ornement
ornamental vine; vitis *[Vitis]* vigne *f* d'ornement
oscillating sprinkler arroseur *m* oscillant
osmanthus *[Osmanthus]* osmanthus *m*
ostrich feather fern; shuttlecock fern *[Matteucia struthiopteris]* fougère plume d'autruche
overripe blet, blette *adj*; surmûri *adj*
oxalis *[Oxalis]* oxalide *f*, oxalide *f* blanche
ox-eye *[Adonis]* adonis *f*
ox-eye daisy *[Bellis]* pâquerette *f*
ox-eye daisy *[Chrysanthemum]* grande marguerite *f*; œil-de-bœuf *m*

P

pachysandra *[Pachysandra]* pachy-sandra
packet of seed sachet *m* de graines
pair of steps escabeau *m*
paling fence clôture *f* en lattis
palm tree palmier *m*
palmette; fan-trained tree palmette *f*
pampas grass *[Cortaderia]* herbe *f* des pampas
pansy *[Viola]* pensée *f*, violette *f* de jardin
papaver *[Papaver]* pavot *m*
parasite parasite *m*
park jardin *m* public
Parma violet *[Viola]* violette *f* de Parme

parsley persil *m*
parsnip panais *m*
parthenocissus *[Parthenocissus]* vigne-vierge *f*
pasque-flower *[Pulsatilla]* pulsatille *f*, anémone *f* pulsatille; coquelourde *f*
passion flower *[Passiflora]* passiflore *f*, fleur *f* de la passion
patch of ground under cultivation plantage *m*; carré *m*
patience (herb); spinach dock [Rumex] patience *f*
paving stone dalle *f*
pea pois *m*
pea pod gousse *f* de pois
pea tree; caragana *[Caragana]* acacia *m* jaune
peach pêche *f*
peach leaf curl cloque *f*; cloque du pêcher
peach-leaved campanula *[Campanula persicifolia]* campanule *f* à feuilles de pêcher
peach tree pêcher *m*
pear poire *f*
pear tree *[Pyrus]* poirier *m*
peat tourbe *f*
peat spade louchet *m*
peaty soil sol *m* tourbeux
pebble caillou *m*; cailloux *mpl*
peg piquet *m*
pelargonium *[Pelargonium]* pélargonium *m*; géranium *m* des fleuristes; géranium des jardins
peony *[Paeonia]* pivoine *f*; rose *f* de Notre-Dame
pennycress *[Thlaspi]* thlaspi *m* des champs
pennywort *[Omphalodes]* gobelets *mpl*; nombril *m* de Venus
perennial; hardy vivace *adj*
perennial plante *f* vivace
perfumed parfumé,-e *adj*
pergola pergola *f*; pergole *f*
periwinkle; vinca *[Vinca]* pervenche *f*
perpetual flowering; remontant remontant *adj*
perpetual flowering rose rosier *m* remontant

persistant leaves; evergreen feuilles *fpl* persistantes
Peruvian lily *[Alstroemeria]* alstrœmère *f*
pesticide pesticide *m*; antinuisible *m*
pests insectes *mpl* nuisibles
petal pétale *m*; feuille *f*
petrol engine mower tondeuse *f* thermique
petunia *[Petunia]* pétunia *m*
pheasant's eye *[Narcissus]* œil *m* de faisan; jeannette *f* blanche; narcisse *m* des poètes
pheasant's eye; adonis *[Adonis]* adonis *f*; goutte-de-sang *f*
phalaris *[Phalaris]* ruban *m* de bergère
phlox *[Phlox]* phlox *m, inv*
phosphate phosphate *m*
phosphorus phosphore *m*
photinia [Photinia] photinia
physalis *[Physalis]* coqueret *m*
pick (to) (flowers, fruit) cueillir *v*
pick; pickaxe pic *m*; pioche *f*
picking (of fruit, vegetables) cueillette *f*
pickling onion petit oignon *m*
pimento poivron *m*
pimpernel *[Anagallis]* baromètre *m* de pauvre homme; anagallide *f*
pinch (to) pincer *v*
pine *[Pinus]* pin *m*
pine, pitch; pine, northern *[Pinus rigida] [Pinus palustris]* pin *m* dur
pine, Scots; pine, Scotch *[Pinus sylvestris]* pin *m* sylvestre
pine needle aiguille *f* de pin
pink; garden pink *[Dianthus plumarius]* mignardise *f*; œillet *m*; œillet *f* mignardise
pip pépin *m*
pipe (to) (carnations) bouturer *v*
piping (of carnations) bouturage *m*
pitcher plant *[Nepenthes]* népenthe *m*; népenthés *m*
pitcher plant; huntsman's horn *[Sarracenia]* sarracénie *f*
plane tree platane *m*
plant plante *f*
plant (to) planter *v*
plant kingdom règne *m* végétal
plant propagation multiplication *f* des plantes

plant sensitive to cold plante *f* frileuse
plantain *[Plantago]* plantain *m*
plantain-lily; funkia *[Funkia]* funkie *f*
planting plantage *m*; plantatation *f*
planting out repiquage *m*
planting season; planting time époque *f* de plantation
plastic pot/container/holder (for plant) godet *m* de plastique
plate grafting greffage *m* en placage
platystemon *[Platystemon]* platystémon *m*
ploughing labourage *m*
plum prune *f*
plum tree *[Prunus]* prunier *m*
plumbago; leadwort; Cape leadwort *[Plumbago capensis]* plumbago *m*; plombago *m*; plumbago *m* du Cap
poet's narcissus *[Narcissus]* narcisse *m* des poètes; œillet *m* de Pâques; jeannette *f* blanche; œil *m* de faisan
poinsettia *[Euphorbia]* poinsettie *f*
poison ivy; poison sumach *[Rhus]* sumac *m* vénéneux
pole pruner échenilloir *m*
polemonium *[Polemonium]* valériane *f* grecque bleue
pollard (to) (a tree) étêter *v*
pollen pollen *m*
pollinate (to) polliniser *v*
pollination pollinisation *f*
polyantha rose rosier *m* polyantha
polyanthus [Primula; Polyanthus] primevère *f* des jardins
polygala *[Polygala]* polygale *m* commun
polygonatum *[Polygonatum]* sceau *m* de Salomon
polygonum *[Polygonum]* renouée *f*
polythene polythène *m*
pomegranate tree; punica *[Punica]* grenadier *m*
pomelo; grapefruit pomelo *m*
pompom; pompon pompon *m*
pompom dahlia *[Dahlia]* dahlia *m* pompon
pompom rose *[Rosa]* rose *f* pompon
pond; pool étang *m*
pondweed épi *m* d'eau; potamot *m*

poor man's weather-glass [Anagallis] baromètre m de pauvre homme

poplar [Populus] peuplier m

poplar, Lombardy [Populus nigra 'italica'] peuplier m d'Italie

poplar, white; poplar, Abele [Populus alba] peuplier m

poppy [Papaver] pavot m; coquelicot m

poppy, Californian [Eschscholtzia] eschscholtzie f

poppy, Californian [Platystemon] platystémon m

Portugal laurel [Prunus] laurier m du Portugal

post poteau m; piquet m

post-hole digger bêche-tarière f

pot (to) empoter v

pot herbs herbes fpl potagères

pot-marigold [Calendula] souci m

pot plant plante f en pot; plante f d'appartement

potash potasse f

potassium potassium m

potato [Solanum tuberosum] pomme f de terre; parmentière f

potato beetle doryphore m

potato blight brunissure f; maladie f des pommes de terre; mildiou m

potato capsid bug [Lygus pabulinus] punaise f de la pomme de terre

potato clamp silo m de pommes de terre

potato hoe croc m à pommes de terre

potato, sweet; Spanish potato patate f

potful; pot potée f

potted plant plante f verte

potting compost terreau m rempotage

potting on rempotage m

potting soil terreau m rempotage

powdery mildew oïdium m

power driven cultivator motoculteur m

prick (of thorn) piqûre f

prick out (to) (seedlings) repiquer v

pricking out repiquage m

prickly épineux,-euse adj; hérissé,-e adj

prickly pear [Opuntia] oponce m; figuier m de Barbarie; raquette f

prickly rhubarb; gunnera [Gunnera] gunnère f

primrose [Primula acaulis] primevère f;

primevère f à grandes fleurs; coucou m

privet; ligustrum [Ligustrum] troène m

produce a crop (to) faire v une recolte

propagate (to) (by cuttings) bouturer v

propagation propagation f

propagation bed couche f de multiplication

propagation by cuttings bouturage m

propagation by root cuttings drageonnage m; propagation f par drageons

protective sacking (round roots of trees for transpantation) tontine f

prune (to) (bush, tree) tailler v

prune (to) élaguer v; émonder v; ébrancher v

prunella [Prunella] brunelle f

pruner; pruning hook émondoir m; ébrancheur m

pruning taille f; émondage m

pruning hook ébranchoir m; émondoir m; élagueur m

pruning knife serpette f

pruning saw scie f d'élagage

pruning shears élagueur m; sécateur m

pruning to ground level nettoyage m des souches

pruning élagage m; ébranchage m

pull up (to); pull out (to) (eg weeds) arracher v

pulsatilla [Pulsatilla (anemone)] coquelourde f

pump pompe f

pumpkin; cucurbita [Cucurbita] potiron m; citrouille f

punnet maniveau m; semelle f à fruits; petit panier m

puny; weedy; stunted chétif,-ive adj

purple foxglove [Digitalis] digitale f (pourprée); digitale pourpre

purple loosestrife; lythrum [Lythrum] salicaire f commune

purslane; portulaca [Portulaca] pourpier m

puschkinia [Puschkinia] puschkinia

push hoe; Dutch hoe binette f à pousser

pyracantha [Pyracantha] buisson m ardente

pyralis; meal moth; bee moth pyrale f

Q

quaking grass; briza *[Briza]* brize *f*;
briza *f*
quenouille-trained fruit tree quenouille *f*
quicklime chaux *f* vive
quince coing *m*
quince tree *[Cydonia]* cognassier *m*
quince (ornamental) *[Chaenomeles]*
cognassier *m* à fleurs; cognassier du
Japon

R

rabbit lapin *m*
radicle radicelle *f*
radish *[Raphanus sativus]* radis *m*
radish, black (winter) radis *m* noir
ragweed ambroisie *f*
ragwort *[Senecio jacobeia]* jacobée *f*;
herbe *f* de saint-Jacques; cinéraire *f*
maritime; séneçon *m*
rake (to); rake up (to) (leaves) ratisser *v*
rake râteau *m*
rake, hay fauchet *m*
rake, tedder râteau-faneur *m*
raking ratissage *m*
rambler rose rosier *m* sarmenteux; rosier
m grimpant
rampant ivy; ground ivy *[Glechoma
hederacea]* lierre *m* terrestre
ranunculus *[Ranunculus]* renoncule *f*
rape colza *m*
raspberry framboise *f*
raspberry bush; raspberry cane; rubus
[Rubus] framboisier *m*
rat rat *m*
rat trap ratière *f*; piège *m* à rats
re-allocation or regrouping of land
remembrement *m* des terres
red cabbage chou *m* rouge; chou *m*
roquette
red campion *[Lychnis]* lychnide *f*
diurne
red currant; white currant bush *[Ribes*

[rubrum]] groseillier *m* à grappes
red pepper; capsicum *[Capsicum]*
piment *m*
red spider araignée *f* rouge
red spider mite (fruit tree) acarien *m*
rouge
red-hot poker *[Kniphofia]* tritome *m*
reed; common reed-grass *[Arundo
Phragmites]* roseau *m* commun
remove (to); cut off (to) (eg dead
flowers) supprimer *v*
remove moss from (to) émousser *v*
replant (to) replanter *v*
repot (to) rempoter *v*
repotting rempotage *m*
reseda *[Reseda]* réséda *m* odorant;
mignonnette *f*
rest harrow; goat root; cammock
[Ononis] bugrane *f*; arrête-bœuf *m*
rhamnus *[Rhamnus]* nerprun *m*
rhizome rhizome *m*
rhododendron *[Rhododendron]*
rhododendron *m*
rhubarb rhubarbe *f*
ribbing plough charrue *f* à soc
ribbon grass *[Phalaris]* ruban *m* de
bergère
rich soil terre *f* riche
ripe mûr *adj*
roadsweeper's broom balai *m* de
cantonnier
robinia *[Robinia]* robinier *m*
rock alyssum *[Alyssum]* thlaspi *m* jaune
rock chamomile; anthemis *[Anthemis]*
anthémis *f*
rock cress *[Aubretia]* aubrétie *f*;
aubretia *f*
rock garden jardin *m* de rocaille; jardin *m*
alpin
rock jasmine; androsace *[Androsace]*
androsace *f* laiteuse
rock rose; cistus *[Cistus]* ciste *m*; ciste
m de Crète
rock rose; helianthemum
[Helianthemum] hélianthème *m*;
helianthemum *m*
rockery; rock garden rocaille *f*; jardin *m*
de rocaille
rocket *[Eruca sativa]* roquette *f*

rodent killer rodonticide *m*
rodgersia *[Rodgersia]* rodgersia
roller rouleau *m*
Roman rocket *[Eruca sativa]* roquette *f*
root racine *f*
root cutting bouture *f* de racine
root out (to); disroot (to) déraciner *v*
root stock souche *f*
root sucker drageon *m*
rootball motte *f* adhérant aux racines
rootlet radicelle *f*
rootstock rhizome *m*; pied *m* mère
rose; rosa *[Rosa]* rose *f*
rose, wild guelder aubour *m*
rose (of hose or watering can) pomme *f*
rose bay; nerium *[Nerium]* laurier-rose
m; rose-laurier *m*
rose campion *[Agrostemma]*
agrostemme *f* en couronne
rose campion *[Lychnis]* coquelourde *f*
des jardins; lychnide *f*, lychnis *m*;
jalousie *f* des jardins
rose chafer; rose beetle cétoine *f* dorée
rose garden roseraie *f*
rose grower rosiériste *m,f*
rose laurel *[Nerium]* laurier-rose *m*;
rose-laurier *m*
rose leaf feuille *f* de rose
rose mallow *[Althaea rosea]* passe-rose
f, rose *f* trémière
rose of Jericho *[Anastatica]* rose *f* de
Jéricho
rose petal feuille *f* de rose
rosebed massif *m* de rosiers
rosebud bouton *m* de rose
rosebush; rose tree rosier *m*
rosehip gratte-cul *m*
rosemary; rosmarinus *[Rosmarinus
officinalis]* romarin *m*; encensier *m*
rot pourriture *f*
rot; rotting pourrissement *m*
rotary hoe bineuse *f* rotative
rotating sprinkler arroseur *m* rotatif
rotation of crops rotation *f* des cultures;
assolement *m*
rotten (fruit) pourri *adj*; gâté *adj*
round shovel pelle *f* ronde
rowan tree; mountain ash *[Sorbus
aucuparia]* sorbier *m* commun; sorbier

des oiseleurs; arbre *m* à grives; cochène
m; sorbier sauvage; sorbier *m* des
oiseaux
royal fern; osmunda *[Osmunda]*
osmonde *f* royale
royal water lily *[Victoria]* victoria *f* regia
rubber boots bottes *fpl* en caoutchouc
rubus *[Rubus]* framboisier *m*
rudbeckia;cone flower; yellow daisy
[Rudbeckia hirta] rudbeckie *f*
rue *[Ruta]* rue *f*
rumex *[Rumex]* oseille *f*
runner coulant *m*; stolon *m*
runner bean haricot *m* à rames; haricot *m*
à filets
ruscus *[Ruscus]* petit houx *m*
rush *[Juncus]* jonc *m*
rustic rustique *adj*
Russian vine *[Polygonum baldschauni-
cum]* renouée *f* de Turkestan
rust rouille *f*

S

sacred bean *[Nelumbium]* lotus *m*
safflower *[Carthamus]* safran *m* bâtard;
carthame *m*
saffron *[Crocus sativus]* safran *m*
saffron, meadow *[Colchicum]* colchique
m automnal; colchique *m* d'automne
sage *[Salvia officinalis]* herbe *f* sacrée;
sauge *f*, sauge *f* officinale
sagebush *[Artemesia]* armoise *f*
sainfoin *[Onobrychis]* sainfoin *m*;
esparcette *f*
saintpaulia *[Saintpaulia]* saintpaulia *f*
sallow-thorn *[Hippophae]* argousier *m*
salpiglossis *[Salpiglossis]* salpiglossis *m*
salsify *[Tragopogon porrifolius]* salsifis
m; barbe-de-bouc *f*
salvia *[Salvia]* salvia *f*, sauge *f* à fleurs
rouges
sand sable *m*
sandwort *[Arenaria]* sabline *f*, arénaire *f*
sandy soil terre *f* sableuse; sol *m*
sablonneux

santolina *[Santolina]* santoline *f*
sanvitalia *[Sanvitalia]* sanvitalia
sap sève *f*
saponaria *[Saponaria]* herbe *f* à foulon;
saponaire *f*
sarracenia *[Sarracenia]* sarracénie *f*
satin flower *[Lunaria]* lunaire *f*;
monnaie-du-pape *f*
satin flower *[Sisyrinchium]*
bermudienne *f*
savory; winter savory *[Satureia
montana]* sarriette *f*
Savoy cabbage chou *m* de Milan;
pancalier *m*
sawfly mouche *f* à scie
saxifrage *[Saxifraga]* saxifrage *f*;
saxifrage *f* ombreuse
saxifrage, burnet *[Pimpinella saxifraga]*
pied-de-chèvre *m*
saxifrage, golden *[Chrysoplenium]*
saxifrage *f* dorée
saxifrage, yellow *[Saxifraga aizoides]*
saxifrage *f* d'automne
scab tavelure *f*
scabious; sweet scabious *[Scabiosa]*
scabieuse *f*
scale insect cochenille *f*
scarifier scarificateur *m*
scarlet pimpernel *[Anagallis]* mouron *m*
rouge; mouron *m* des champs
scarlet runner haricot *m* d'Espagne
scent parfum *m*
scented parfumé,-e *adj*
scilla *[Scilla]* scille *f*
scion scion *m*; ente *f*; greffe *f*; greffon *m*
scirpus *[Scirpus]* scirpe *m*
scolopendra scolopendre *f*
scorpion grass *[Myosotis]* myosotis *m*
scuffle hoe ratissoire *f*
scythe faux *f*; faucille *f*
scythe (to); mow (to) faucher *v*
sea holly; eryngium *[Eryngium]*
panicaut *m*; panicaut *m* maritime
sea lavender *[Statice limonium]*
statice *m*
sea rocket roquette *f* de mer
sea thrift; sea pink *[Statice limonium]*
statice *m*
sea-buckthorn; hippophae *[Hippophae]*

argousier *m*
secateur; (pair of) secateurs sécateur *m*
sedge; carex *[Carex]* laîche *f*
sedum *[Sedum]* orpin *m*
seed graine *f*; semence *f*
seed and fertilizer drill semoir *m* à
engrais
seed box germoir *m*
seed (grape, apple etc) pépin *m*
seed merchant (person) grainetier *m*;
grainetière *f*
seed merchant (shop) graineterie *f*
seed pod péricarpe *m*
seed potato pomme *f* de terre de
semence
seed tray caissette *f* à semis; germoir *m*
seedbed semis *m; couche f*
seeding ensemencement *m*
seeding machine semoir *m*; semoir *m*
mécanique
seedless sans pépins *adj*
seedling semis *m;* plant *m*; jeune plant *m*
selective weed-killer désherbant *m*
sélectif
self heal *[Prunella]* brunelle *f*
sempervivum *[Sempervivum]* joubarbe *f*
send out (to) (eg shoots); give out (to)
émettre *v*
service tree, wild *[Sorbus torminalis]*
alisier *m* torminal
Seville orange tree; bitter orange tree
[Citrus Bigaradia] bigaradier *m*
shallot échalote *f* à maturité
shear or clip (to) tondre *v*
shears; garden shears cisaille *f* de
jardin
shears; pruning shears cisailles *fpl*
shed its petals (to) s'effeuiller *v*
shed remise *f*
shed; lean-to; outhouse; warehouse
hangar *m*
shepherd's purse *[Capsella]*
bourse-à-pasteur *f*
shieldbud (for grafting) écusson *m*
shoot rejet *m*
shoot (to); sprout (to) pousser *v*;
bourgeonner *v*
short shoot lambourde *f*; dard *m*
shovel pelle *f*

shredder broyeur *m* de végétaux
shrub arbuste *m*; arbrisseau *m*
Siberian iris *[Iris]* iris *m* de Sibérie
sickle faucille *f*
sidalcea *[Sidalcea]* sidalcée *f*;
sidalcea *m*
side-saddle flower *[Sarracenia]*
sarracénie *f*
silene *[Silene]* silène *m*
silver birch; common birch; European
birch *[Betula pendula]* bouleau *m*
silver willow; white willow *[Salix alba]*
saule *m* blanc
sisyrinchium *[Sisyrinchium]*
bermudienne *f*
sit-on lawn mower tondeuse *f*
autoportée
skimmia *[Skimmia]* skimmia
slaked lime chaux *f* éteinte
slipper flower; slipperwort *[Calceolaria]*
calcéolaire *f*
sloe prunelle *f*
sloe bush *[Prunus spinosa]* prunellier *m*;
épine *f* noire
slug bait appât *m* antilimaces
slug pellets granulés *mpl* antilimaces;
antilimaces *fpl* compo
slug; slugs limace *f* du sol; limaces *fpl*
small hand cultivator griffe *f* à fleurs
small hoe houette *f*
smoke tree; cotinus *[Cotinus]* arbre *m* à
perruque
snail; garden snail escargot *m*
snake's beard; ophiopogon
[Ophiopogon] herbe *f* aux turquoises
snake's head; chequered daffodil
[Fritillaria] fritillaire *f* méléagride;
fritillaire *f* damier
snapdragon *[Antirrhinum]*
gueule-de-loup *f*
snowberry *[Symphoricarpos]*
symphorine *f*
snowdrop; galanthus *[Galanthus
nivalis]* perce-neige *m, inv*
snowflakes; leucojum *[Leucojum]*
nivéole *f*
snow-in-summer *[Cerastium
tomentosum]* corbeille-de-la-mariée *f*
soak (to); drench (to) tremper *v*

soapwort *[Saponaria]* saponaire *f*;
herbe *f* à foulon
sodden soil; waterlogged soil sol *m*
détrempé
soft fruit baies *fpl* comestibles; fruits *mpl*
charnus; fruits *mpl* rouges
soft shield fern; hedge fern *[Poly-
stichum setiferum]* fougère *f* aspidie
soil sol *m*; terre *f*; terroir *m*
soil acidity acidité *f* d'un sol
solanum *[Solanum]* solanacée *f*
solidago *[Solidago]* solidage *f*
Solomon's seal *[Polygonatum]* sceau *m*
de Salomon
sorghum; Indian millet sorgho *m*
sorrel *[Rumex]* oseille *f*
sow (to) (seed) semer *v*
sow thinly (to) semer *v* à claire-voie
sowing semis *m*
sowing machine semoir *m* mécanique;
semoir *m*
spade bêche *f*
spading fork fourche *f* à bêcher
Spanish broom *[Genista]* genêt *m*
d'Espagne
Spanish chestnut tree; sweet chestnut
tree *[Constanea sativa]* châtaignier *m*;
châtaignier *m* commun; marronnier *m*
Spanish onion oignon *m* d'Espagne
speedwell *[Veronica]* véronique *f*
spicule épillet *m*
spider araignée *f*
spider, red araignée *f* rouge
spiderwort; tradescantia *[Tradescantia]*
éphémère *f*; éphémère *f* de Virginie;
tradescantie *f* de Virginie
spike épi *m*
spikelet épillet *m*
spinach épinard *m*
spinach dock *[Rumex]* patience *f*
spindle-tree; euonymus *[Euonymus]*
fusain *m*
spiraea *[Spiraea]* spirée *f*
spleenwort; asplenium *[Asplenium]*
doradille *f*
spots; speckles (on fruit) tavelure *f*
spray (to) (lawn etc) arroser *v*
spray of blossom une petite branche *f*
fleuri; rameau *m* en fleurs

sprayer vaporisateur *m*
sprayer; tank sprayer pulvérisateur *m*
spraying (lawn etc) arrosage *m*;
  arrosement *m*
spread (to) épandre *v*
spread out (to) étaler *v*
spreader épandeur *m*
spring printemps *m*
spring printanier,-ière *adj*
spring (water) source *f*
spring beetle taupin *m*
spring crocus *[Crocus albiflorus]* safran
  m printanier
spring onion échalote *f* nouvelle
sprinkle (to) arroser *v*
sprinkler arroseur *m*
sprinkling arrosage *m*; arrosement *m*
sprinkler hose tuyau *m* perforé
sprout; young shoot pousse *f*
spruce, Norway; fir, white *[Picea abies]*
  épicéa *m* commun; sapin *m* de Norvège;
  sapin blanc
spur pruning taille *f* fruitière
spurge; euphorbia *[Euphorbia]*
  euphorbe *f*; cierge *m*
spurge-laurel *[Daphne]* daphné *m*
  morillon
squill; bluebell [Scilla] scille *f*
squirrel écureil *m*
St. Bernard's lily *[Anthericum]*
  phalangère *f* à fleur de lis
St. John's Wort; Aaron's Beard; Rose
  of Sharon; Tutsan *[Hypericum]*
  millepertuis *m*; herbe-à-mille-trous
St. Peter's wort; symphoricarpos
  [Symphoricarpos] symphorine *f*
stake; support étai *m*; tuteur *m*; piquet *m*
stake (for vine) échalas *m* de vigne
stake (to) tuteurer *v*; étayer *v*
staking étayage *m*
staking (of plants) tuteurage *m*
stalk (of plant) tige *f*
stamen étamine *f*
standard (tree) haute-tige *m*; arbre *m* en
  haute-tige
standard rose rosier *m* tige; rosier à tige;
  rosier sur tige; rosier haute tige
star of Bethlehem *[Ornithogalum]*
  ornithogale *m* à ombelle

star of the Veldt [Dimorphotheca]
  dimorphotheca
starflower *[Trientalis]* trientale *f*
  d'Europe
statice *[Statice limonium]* statice *m*
stem tige *f*
stephanotis *[Stephanotis floribunda]*
  jasmin *m* de Madagascar
stepladder escabeau *m*
stick; prop (for peas, etc) rame *f*
stinging nettle *[Urtica]* ortie *f* brûlante;
  ortie *f* romaine
stock *[Matthiola]* giroflée *f* des jardins;
  grande giroflée *f*
stock, ten-week *[Matthiola]* giroflée *f*
  quarantaine
stock; rootstock; understock
  porte-greffe *m,inv*
Stoke's aster; stokesia *[Stokesia]*
  stokesia
stone; pebble caillou *m*; cailloux *mpl*
stonecrop *[Sedum]* orpin *m*
stony ground terrain *m* pierreux
stony soil sol *m* pierreux
stool pied *m* mère
straw paille *f*
straw mat paillasson *m*
strawberry fraise *f*
strawberry bed fraiseraie *f*; fraisière *f*
strawberry plant *[Fragaria]* fraisier *m*
strawberry tree; arbutus *[Arbutus]* arbre
  m à fraises; arbousier *m*; arbousier *m*
  commun
strike roots (to) prendre *v* racine
strimmer coupe-herbe *m* à fil
string fil *m*; cordeau *m*
striped squill [Puschkinia] puschkinia
stump (tree, etc) souche *f*
succulent succulent *adj*
succulent (plant) plante *f* grasse
sucker surgeon *m*; drageon *m*; stolon *m*;
  gourmand *m*
sulphur soufre *m*
sumach; rhus *[Rhus]* sumac *m*
summer été *m*
summer estival *adj*
summer cypress *[Kochia]*
  faux-conifère *m*
summer heather; calluna *[Calluna]*

61

bruyère *f* d'été
summer pruning taille *f* en vert; taille
d'été
sun rose *[Helianthemum]* hélianthème *m*
sundew; youth wort *[Drosera]* rossolis
m; rosée *f* de soleil; drosère *f*, droséra *f*
sunflower *[Helianthus]* tournesol *m*;
soleil *m*; soleil *m* vivace; hélianthe *m*;
helianthus *m*
superphosphate of lime
superphosphate *m* de chaux
swallow wort *[Asclepias]*
herbe-aux-perruches *f*
swede; Swedish turnip rutabaga *m*
sweet Alison *[Alyssum]* corbeille *f*
d'argent
sweet bay *[Laurus nobilis]* laurier *m*
commun; laurier noble; laurier d'Apollon
sweet bent *[Luzula]* luzule *f* des champs
sweet corn maïs *m*
sweet flag *[Acorus]* acore *m*
sweet gale; bog myrtle; Dutch myrtle
[Myrica gale] myrte *m* des marais
sweet grass; glyceria *[Glyceria]*
glycérie *f*
sweet pea *[Lathyrus odoratus]* pois *m* de
senteur; gesse *f* odorante
sweet pepper poivron *m*; piment *m*
sweet rocket *[Hesperis]* julienne *f* des
dames
sweet rush, acorus *[Acorus]* acore *m*
sweet sultan *[Centaurea]* centaurée *f*
musquée
sweet William *[Dianthus]* œillet *m* barbu;
œillet *m* de poète
Swiss chard bette *f*
sycamore; sycamore maple *[Acer
pseudoplatanus]* sycomore *m*; érable *m*
sycomore; faux platane *m*
syringa *[Philadelphus]* seringa *m*;
seringat *m*
systemic fungicide fongicide *m*
systémique

T

tagetes *[Tagetes]* œillet *m* d'Inde
tamarisk; tamarix *[Tamarix]* tamaris *m*
tansy; alecust *[Tanacetum]* tanaisie *f*
taproot pivot *m*; racine *f* pivotante
tarragon *[Artemisia]* estragon *m*;
dragonne *f*; serpentine *f*
taxus *[Taxus]* if *m*
tea plant *[Camellia]* théier *m*
tea rose *[Rosa]* rose-thé *f*
tecoma *[Tecoma]* jasmin *m* de Virginie
tedder rake râteau-faneur *m*
tegument; seed coat tégument *m*
tendril griffe *f*
ten-week stock *[Matthiola]* giroflée *f*
quarantaine
tendril vrille *f*
thalictrum *[Thalictrum]* pigamon *m* des
prés
thin out (to) (seedlings, hedge)
éclaircir *v*
thistle chardon *m*
thlaspi, candytuft; iberis *[Iberis]*
thlaspi *m*
thorn épine *f*
thorn apple; datura *[Datura]* datura *m*
thornless sans épines *adj*; inerme *adj*
thorny épineux,-euse *adj*
three-pronged cultivator griffe *f* trois
dents
three-tined soil levelling hook croc *m* à
rosiers
thrift *[Armeria]* armeria *f*; armérie *f*;
armeria *f* commune; gazon *m* d'Espagne
thrips thrips *m*
thunbergia *[Thunbergia]* thunbergie *f*
thuya; thuja *[Thuya]* thuia *m*; thuya *m*
thyme thym *m*
tiarella *[Tiarella]* tiarella *m*; tiarelle *f*
tickseed *[Coreopsis]* coréopsis *m*
tiger iris; tigridia *[Tigridia]*
œil-de-paon *m*
tiger lily *[Lilium]* lis *m* tigré; lis *m* orangé
tilling labourage *m*
tip (to) pincer *v*
toadflax; linaria *[Linaria]* velvote *f*;

linaire *f*; linaire commune
toadflax (ii) *[Linaria]* éperonnière *f*
tobacco plant *[Nicotiana]* tabac *m*
d'ornement
tomato tomate *f*
tongue-flowered orchid *[Serapias]*
helléborine *f*
tool shed abri *m* de jardin; remise *f*
toothwort *[Dentaria]* dentaire *f* à neuf
feuilles
top (off) (to); poll (to) écimer *v*
top graft (to) regreffer *v*
top shoot; terminal shoot pousse *f*
terminale
topiary topiare *f*; taille *f* ornamentale des
arbres
topping (off); polling écimage
torch lily *[Kniphofia]* tritome *m*
torch thistle [Cereus] cierge *m*
tractor tracteur *m*
tradescantia *[Tradescantia]*
tradescantie *f* de Virginie
trailer remorque *f*
trailer spreader épandeur *m* à tracter
training by nailing up trailing plants etc
palissage *m*
transplanter; transplanting machine
transplantoir *m*
trap; snare piège *m*
traveller's joy; clematis *[Clematis]*
clématite *f* des haies
treasure flower [Gazania] gazania
treat with mould (to) (plant, ground)
terreauter *v*
tree arbre *m*
tree daphne: pittosporum *[Pittosporum]*
pittosporum *m*
tree mallow; lavatera *[Lavatera]*
lavatère *f* en arbre
tree nursery pépinière *f* fruitière
tree pruner échenilloir-élagueur *m;*
échenilloir *m*
tree saw scie *f* à bûches
tree-lined bordé d'arbres *adj*
trellis; trellising treillage *m*
triennial trisannuel *adj*
trim (to) émonder *v*; tailler *v*)
trim (to) (roots) habiller *v*
trumpet creeper *[Tecoma]* jasmin *m*

trompette; jasmin *m* de Virginie
trumpet flower; bignonia *[Bignonia]*
bignone *f*; bignonia *m*
trumpet flower *[Tecoma]* jasmin *m*
trompette; jasmin *m* de Virginie
trunk; tree trunk tronc *m* d'arbre
tub bac *m* à plante
tuber tubercule *m*
tuberose *[Polyanthes]* tubéreuse *f*
tulip *[Tulipa]* tulipe *f*
tulip tree tulipier *m*
turf gazon *m*
turf (single) motte *f* de gazon
turf border cordon *m* de gazon
turn over (to) bêcher *v*
turnip navet *m*
turnip tops fanes *fpl* de navets
twig rameau *m*; brindille *f*
twining volubile *adj*
twitch chiendent *m* (officinal)
two handed secateur sécateur *m* à deux
mains
two-pronged hoe binoche *f*

UV

umbellate parasol (en)
undergrowth broussaille *f*
undergrowth strimmer débrous -
sailleuse *f*
unfold (to); open out (to) déplier *v*; se
déplier *v*
ungrafted franc de pied
ungrafted tree; maiden tree arbre *m*
franc de pied
universal insecticide insecticide *m*
polyvalent
valerian *[Valeriana]* valériane *f*
variegated panaché *adj*
variety variété *f*
vegetable légume *m*
vegetable garden jardin *m* potager;
potager *m*
vegetable farming; vegetable growing
culture *f* maraîchère
vegetable grower producteur *m*;

maraîcher *m*; jardinier *m* maraîcher
vegetable growing maraîchage *m*
vegetable growing under glass culture
f maraîchère sous verre
vegetable kingdom règne *m* végétal
vegetable mould terre *f* franche
vegetable or herb plante *f* potagère
vegetable plot plant *m* de légumes
vegetation waste déchets *mpl* végetaux
verbascum *[Verbascum]* molène *f*;
cierge *m*
verbena; vervain *[Verbena]* verveine *f*
viburnum *[Viburnum]* boule-de-neige *f*
veronica *[Veronica]* véronique *f*
vetch; everlasting pea *[Lathyrus]*
gesse *f*
viburnum *[Viburnum]* viorne *f*
vine; grapevine vigne *f*; vigne *f* à raisin
vine leaf feuille *f* de vigne
vine mildew oïdium *m*
viola *[Viola]* violette *f* de jardin; pansée *f*
violet *[Viola]* violette *f*
viper's bugloss *[Echium]* vipérine *f*;
herbe *f* aux vipères
Virginia creeper *[Parthenocissus]*
vigne-vierge *f*
viscum *[Viscum]* gui *m*
vitex *[Vitex]* vitex *m*
vole; field-vole campagnol *m*

W

wake robin; wild arum *[Arum]* arum *m*;
pied-de-veau *m*; gouet *m* d'Italie
wallflower *[Cheiranthus]* baguette *f* d'or;
violier *m* jaune; ravenelle *f*; giroflée *f*
jaune; giroflée *f* des murailles
walnut noix *f*
walnut tree *[Juglans regia]* noix *f*; noyer
m commun
walnut, black *[Juglans nigra]* noyer *m*
noir
wall cress *[Arabis]* arabis *f*; arabette *f*
wasp guêpe *f*
wasp's nest guêpier *m*
water (to) arroser *v*

water agrimony *[Eupatorium]* chanvre *m*
d'eau
water bean; nelumbium *[Nelumbium]*
lotus *m*
water cress cresson *m* de fontaine
water crowfoot *[Ranunculus]*
grenouillet *f*
water hyacinth *[Eichornia]* jacinthe *f*
d'eau
water lily; nenuphar *[Nuphar]*
nénuphar *m*
water lily *[Nymphaea]* nymphéa *m*; lis *m*
des étangs
water plantain; alisma *[Alisma]* plantain
m d'eau
water spike potamot *m*
watering can arrosoir *m*
watering arrosage *m*; arrosement *m*
weed (to) désherber *v*; sarcler *v*
weed-killer herbicide *adj & m*;
désherbant *m*
weed-killing désherbage *m*
weed lifter croc *m* à sarcler
weeder tire-racines *m*
weeding sarclage *m*
weeding hoe sarcloir *m*
weeding machine; weeder
désherbeuse *f*
weeding désherbage *m*
weeds mauvaises herbes *fpl*
weeping rose rosier *m* pleureur
weeping willow saule *m* pleurer
weevil charançon *m*
weigela; bush honeysuckle *[Weigela or
Diervilla]* weigelie *f*
well puits
wet rot pourriture *f* humide; carie *f*
humide
wheelbarrow brouette *f*
whitebeam *[Sorbus aria]* alisier *m* blanc
white cabbage chou *m* pommé blanc
white lily *[Lilium]* lis *m* blanc
white oxeye; oxeye daisy
[Chrysanthemum] œil-de-bœuf *m*
white satin *[Lunaria]* satin *m* blanc
white water lily *[Nymphaea]* nymphéa *m*
blanc
white willow *[Salix alba]* saule *m* blanc
whitefly (greenhouse) aleurode *m* des

serres; mouche *f* blanc des serres
whitethorn *[Crataegus oxycantha]*
aubépine *f*
whortleberry myrtille *f*
whortleberry bush; bilberry bush
[Vaccinium myrtillus] myrtillier *m*
wig sumac *[Cotinus]* arbre *m* à perruque
wild camomile matricaire *f* camomille
**wild celery; lovage; smallage; water
parsley** *[Levisticum]* ache *f*; livèche *f*;
céleri *m* vivace
wild ginger *[Asarum]* asaret *m*
wild heliotrope; phacelia *[Phacelia]*
phacélie *f*
wild hyacinth *[Hyacinthus]* jacinthe *f*
des bois; jacinthe *f* sauvage
wild marjoram; origano *[Origanum
vulgare]* origan *m*
wild orchid orchis *m*
wild radish ravenelle *f*
wild rose *[Rosa canina]* rose *f* de chien;
églantine *f*
wild rosemary; andromeda
[Andromeda] andromède *f*
wild stock (for grafting sauvageon *m*
wild strawberry fraise *f* des bois; fraise *f*
sauvage
willow *[Salix]* saule *m*
willow, crack; willow, brittle *[Salis
fragilis]* saule *m* cassant; saule *m* fragile
**willow, goat; willow, pussy sallow;
willow, grey** *[Salix caprea]* saule *m*
marsault; marsault *m*
willow, white *[Salix alba]* saule *m*
argenté
willow herb *[Epilobium]* épilobe *m*;
épilobe *m* à épi; laurier *m* de
Saint-Antoine; osier *m* fleuri
wilt (to) (flower) flétrir *v*; se flétrir *v*;
faner *v*; se faner *v*
wind break brise-vent *m,inv*; abat-vent *m,
inv*; volis *m*; chablis *m*
windfalls fruits *mpl* décidus; fruits *mpl*
tombés
windflower *[Gentiana]* gentiane *f* des
marais
winter hiver *m*
winter hivernal *adj*
winter aconite; eranthis *[Eranthis*

hyemalis] éranthe *m*; hellébore *m*
d'hiver
winter cabbage chou *m* d'hiver
winter garden; conservatory jardin *m*
d'hiver
winter heath; erica *[Erica]* bruyère *f*
d'hiver
winter heliotrope *[Petasites]* pétasite *m*
winter jasmine *[Jasminum]* jasmin *m*
d'hiver
winter pruning taille *f* en sec; taille *f*
d'hiver
wintergreen *[Pyrola]* pyrole *f*
wintergreen *[Trientalis]* trientale *f*
d'Europe
wintering (eg of plants under cover)
hivernage *m* sous abri
wire netting grillage *m*
wireworm larve *f* de taupin
wistaria; wisteria *[Wistaria]* glycine *f*;
glycine *f* de Chine; glycine *f* de Japon;
wistarie *f*
witch-hazel *[Hamamelis]* noisetier *m* de
sorcière; hamamélis *m*
wither (to) (plant) dessécher *v*; se
dessécher *v*; flétrir *v*; se flétrir *v*
withered desséché *adj*; fané *adj*; flétri *adj*
withering dépérissement *m*
wolfsbane *[Aconitum]* aconit *m*
wood anemone *[Anemone]* sylvie *f*
wood saw scie *f* à bois
wood sorrel; oxalis *[Oxalis]* oxalide *f*;
oxalide *f* blanche; petite oseille *f*; pain *m*
de coucou
woodbine; lonicera *[Lonicera]*
chèvrefeuille *m*
woodlouse cloporte *m*
woodruff *[Asperula]* aspérule *f* odorante
woodwaxen; woadwaxen *[Genista
tinctoria]* herbe-à-jaunir *f*
woodworm ver *m* du bois
working the ground manutention *f* de
terre
worm; earthworm ver *m* de terre;
lombric *m*
wound wort; stachys *[Stachys]* épiaire
f; stachyde *f*

Y

yarrow *[Achillea]* achillée *f*
yellow (to); turn yellow (to) jaunir *v*
yellow asphodel *[Asphodelus luteus]*
bâton *m* de Jacob;
yellow balsam [Balsam] balsamine *f*
yellow balsam; touch-me-not
[Impatiens noli-me-tangere]
ne-me-touchez-pas *m*
yellow chrysanthemum
[Chrysanthemum segetum] marguerite *f*
dorée
yellow iris *[Iris]* iris *m* jaune des marais
yellow ox-eye *[Chrysanthemum*
segetum] marguerite *f* dorée
yellow pimpernel *[Lysimachia]*
lysimachie *f*; lysimaque *f*
yellow saxifrage *[Saxifraga aizoides]*
saxifrage *f* d'automne
yellow star of Bethlehem *[Gagea]*
étoile *f* jaune
yellow water lily; spatter dock *[Nuphar*
lutea] nénuphar *m* jaune; nénuphar des
étangs; lis *m* jaune
yellowweed *[Reseda luteola]*
herbe-à-jaunir *f*
yew; yew tree *[Taxus]* if *m*
young plant plant *m*; jeune plant *m*
yucca [Yucca] yucca *m*

Z

Zanzibar balsam; busy Lizzie
[Impatiens] impatiens *f*
Zanzibar water lily *[Nymphaea]*
nymphéa *m* de Zanzibar
zinnia *[Zinnia]* zinnia *m*
zuchini courgette *f*

BUTTERFLIES OF FRANCE

admiral, red	vulcain m; amiral m	[Vanessa atalanta]
admiral, southern white	sylvain m azuré	[Ladoga reducta]
admiral, white	petit sylvain m; amiral m blanc	[Ladoga camilla]
apollo	apollon m	[Parnassius apollo]
apollo, small	petit apollon m	[Parnassius phoebus]
blue, chalk-hill	argus m bleu nacré	[Lysandra coridon]
blue, common	azuré m commun	[Polyommatus icarus]
blue, Damon	sablé m du sanfoin	[Agrodiaetus damon]
blue, holly	argus m bleu	[Celastrina argiolus]
blue, small	argus m minime	[Cupido minimus]
brimstone	citron m	[Gonepteryx rhamni]
brown, meadow	myrtil m	[Maniola jurtina]
brown, wall	satyre m	[Lasiommata megera]
Cleopatra	citron m de Provence	[Gonepteryx cleopatra]
copper, small	bronzé m	[Lycaena phlaeas]
Escher's blue	grand argus m	[Agrodiaetus escheri]
fritillary	argynne m	[Argynnis]
fritillary, Glanville	damier m	[Melitaea cinxia]
fritillary, pearl-bordered	collier m argenté	[Clossiana euphrosyne]
fritillary, silver-washed	argynne m tabac d'Espagne;	[Argynnis paphia]
	empereur m	
gatekeeper; hedge brown	amaryllis f	[Pyronia tithonus]
grayling, great banded	silène m	[Brintesia circe]
hairstreak, green	thécla m de la ronce	[Callophrys rubi]
hairstreak, purple	thécla m du chêne	[Quercusia quercus]
heath, small	procris m	[Coenonympha pamphilus]
lime hawkmoth	sphinx m du tilleul	[Mimas tiliae]
map butterfly	carte f géographique	[Araschnia levana]
Oberthur's grizzled skipper	hespéne des potentilles	[Pyrgus armoricanus]
orange-tip	aurore f	[Anthocharis cardamines]
pale clouded yellow	soufré m	[Colias hyale]
peacock butterfly	paon m du jour	[Inachis io]
ringlet	tristan m	[Aphantopus hyperantus]
ringlet, Dewy	grand negre m	[Erebia pandrose]
silver-spotted skipper	virgule f	[Hesperia comma]
Spanish festoon	prospérine f	[Zerynthia rumina]
speckled wood	tircis m	[Pararge aegeria]
swallowtail	grand porte-queue m,inv;	[Papilio machaon]
	machaon m	
tortoiseshell, large	grande tortue f	[Nymphalis polychloros]
tortoiseshell, small	petite tortue f	[Aglais urticae]
white, black-veined	piéride f gazée	[Aporia crataegi]
white, green-veined	piéride f du navet	[Pieris napi]
white, large; cabbage white	piéride f du chou	[Pieris brassicae]
white, marbled	demideuil m	[Melanargia galanthea]
white, small	piéride f de la rave	[Pieris rapae]
white ermine moth	écaille f tigrée	[Spilosoma lubricipeda]

BIRDS OF FRANCE

alpine swift	martinet m alpin	[Apus melba]
barn owl	chouette f effraie	[Tyto alba]
bee-eater	guêpier m d'Europe	[Merops apiaster]
blackbird	merle m noir	[Turdus merula]
blue tit	mésange f bleue	[Parus caeruleus]
chough	crave m à bec rouge	[Pyrrhocorax pyrrhocorax]
coal tit	mésange f noire	[Parus ater]
corn bunting	bruant m proyer	[Emberiza calandra]
crow, carrion	corneille f noire	[Corvus corone corone]
cuckoo	coucou m gris	[Cuculus canorus]
dove, collared	tourterelle f turque	[Streptopelia decaocto]
dove, turtle	tourterelle f des bois	[Streptopelia turtur]
eagle owl	hibou m grand-duc	[Bubo bubo]
egret, little	aigrette f garzette	[Egretta garzetta]
golden oriole	loriot m	[Oriolus oriolus]
great tit	mésange f charbonnière	[Parus major]
house martin	hirondelle f de fenêtre	[Delichon urbica]
jackdaw	choucas m des tours; chouchette f	[Corvus monedula]
jay	geai m des chênes	[Garrulus glandarius]
kingfisher	martin-pêcheur m	[Alcedo atthis]
lark, crested	cochevis m huppé	[Galerida cristata]
linnet	linotte f mélodieuse	[Acanthis cannabina]
long-tailed tit	mésange f à longue queue	[Aegithalos caudatus]
magpie	pie f bavarde	[Pica pica]
mallard	canard m colvert	[Anas platyrhynchos]
nightingale	rossignol m philomèle	[Luscinia megarhynchos]
nightjar	engoulevent m d'Europe	[Caprimulgus europaeus]
nutcracker	casse-noix m,inv moucheté	[Nucifraga caryocatactes]
nuthatch	sittelle f torchepot	[Sitta europaea]
owl, little	chouette f chevêche	[Athene noctua]
owl, long-eared	hibou m moyen-duc	[Asio otus]
owl, tawny	chouette f hulotte	[Strix aluco]
oystercatcher	huitrier pie f	[Haematopus ostralegus]
partridge	perdrix f grise	[Perdix perdix]
pheasant	faisan m de chasse	[Phasianus colchicus]
raven	grand corbeau m	[Corvus corax]
robin; redbreast	rouge-gorge m	[Erithacus rubecula]
rook	corbeau m freux	[Corvus frugilegus]
sand martin	hirondelle f de rivage	[Riparia riparia]
skylark	alouette f des champs	[Alauda arvensis]
sparrow, house	moineau m domestique	[Passer domesticus]
sparrow, tree	moineau m friquet	[Passer montanus]
sparrowhawk	épervier m d'Europe	[Accipiter nisus]
starling	étourneau m sansonnet	[Sturnus vulgaris]
swallow	hirondelle f de cheminée	[Hirundo rustica]
swift	martinet m noir	[Apus apus]

teal	sarcelle *f* d'hiver	*[Anas crecca]*
thrush, mistle	grive *f* draine	*[Turdus viscivorus]*
thrush, song	grive *f* musicienne	*[Turdus philomelos]*
warbler, reed	rousserolle *f* effarvatte	*[Acrocephalus scirpaceus]*
woodlark	alouette *f* lulu	*[Lullula arborea]*
woodpecker, great-spotted	pic *m* épeiche	*[Dendrocopus major]*
woodpecker, green	pic *m* vert	*[Picus viridis]*
woodpecker, lesser spotted	pic *m* épeichette	*[Dendrocopus minor]*
woodpigeon	pigeon *m* ramier	*[Columba palumbus]*
wryneck	torcol *m* fourmilier;	*[Jynx torquilla]*
torcou *m*		
yellowhammer	bruant *m* jaune	*[Emberiza citrinella]*

69

LES PLANTES MÉDICINALES
MEDICINAL PLANTS

ail *m*	garlic	*Allium sativum*
ananas *m*	pineapple	*Ananas comosus*
angelique *f*	wild angelica	*Angelica sylvestris*
armoise *f*	artemisia	*Artemisia vulgaris*
arnica *f*	arnica	*Arnica montana*
artichaut *m*	globe artichoke	*Cynara scolymus*
aubépine *f*	hawthorn	*Crataegus oxycantha*
badiane *f*; anis m étoilé	star anise; Chinese anise	*Illicium anisatum*
basilic *m*	basil	*Ocimum basilicum*
bigarade *f*	Seville orange; bitter orange	*Citrus aurantium*
boldo *m*	boldo	*Peumus boldus*
bouleau *m*	silver birch	*Betula pendula*
bourdaine *f*	alder buckthorne	*Frangula alnus*
bourrache *f* officinale	borage	*Borago officinalis*
bugrane *f*	restharrow	*Ononis spinosa*
camomille *f* allemande	German camomile	*Matricaria chamomilla*
cassis *m*	blackcurrant	*Ribes nigrum*
chiendent *m*	couch grass	*Agropyron repens*
chrysanthème *m* des prés	oxeye daisy	*Chrysanthemum leucanthemum*
citron *m*	lemon	*Citrus limon*
coquelicot *m*	corn poppy	*Papaver rhoeas*
cyprès *m*	Italian cypress	*Cupressus sempervirens*
dent-de-lion *f*	dandelion	*Taraxacum officinale*
escholtzie *f*	California poppy	*Eschscholtzia californica*
fenouil *m*	fennel	*Anethum foeniculum*
fenugrec *m*	fenugreek	*Trigonella foenumgraecum*
frêne *m*	ash	*Fraxinus excelsior*
garcinia *m* / guttier *m*	gamboge	*Garcinia Cambogia*
gentiane *f* jaune	yellow gentian	*Gentiana lutea*
ginkgo biloba *m*	gingko biloba	*Gingko biloba*
ginseng *m*	gingseng	*Panax ginseng*
genévrier *m*	juniper	*Juniperus communis*
griffe *f* du diable (harpagophytum)	devil's claw	*Harpagophytum procumbens*
groseiller *m* rouge	red currant	*Ribes rubrum*
hamamélis *m*	witch hazel	*Hamamelis virginiana*
lavande *f*	lavender	*Lavandula spica*
marron *m* d'Inde	horse chestnut	*Aesculus hippocastanum*
mélilot *m*	yellow melilot; sweet clover	*Melilotus officinalis*
mélisse *f*	balm	*Melissa officinalis*
menthe *f* poivrée	peppermint	*Mentha x piperita*
millefeuille *m*	milfoil; yarrow	*Achillea millefolium*
millepertuis *m*	St. John's Wort	*Hypericum perforatum*
myrtille *f*	bilberry; whortleberry	*Vaccinium Myrtillus*
onagre *f*	evening primrose	*Oenothera biennis*
origan *m*	marjoram	*Origanum vulgare*
ortie *f* piquante	stinging nettle	*Urtica dioca*

passiflore f	passiflore; passion flower	*Passiflora incarnata*
pensée f sauvage	heartsease; pansy	*Viola tricolor*
petite pervenche f	lesser periwinkle	*Vinca minor*
plantain m majeur	greater plantain	*Plantago major*
prêle f	horse-tail	*Equisetum arvense*
raisin d'ours m	bearberry	*Arctostaphylos uvi-ursi*
reine f des prés	meadowsweet	*Spiraea ulmaria*
rhubarbe f	rhubarb	*Rheum palmatum*
réglisse f	liquorice	*Glycyrrhiza glabra*
romarin m	rosemary	*Rosmarinus officinalis*
salsepareille f	sarsaparilla	*Smilax aspera*
sauge f	common sage	*Salvia officinalis*
saule m blanc	white willow	*Salix alba*
sené m	senna	*Cassia angustifolia*
valériane f	valerian	*Valeriana officinalis*
vergerette f de Canada	Canadian fleabane	*Erigeron Canadensis*
vigne f rouge	vine	*Vitis vinifera*

HADLEY PAGER INFO PUBLICATIONS
French-English, English-French

GLOSSARY OF HOUSE PURCHASE AND RENOVATION TERMS

Paperback, 2000, Fourth Edition, 56 pages, 210 x 148 mm
ISBN 1-872739-08-3   Price: £7.50
- Provides over 2000 French words and phrases used by estate agents, notaires, mortgage lenders, builders, decorators, etc.

GLOSSARY OF FRENCH LEGAL TERMS

Paperback, 1999, 114 pages, 210 x 148 mm
ISBN 1-872739-07-5   Price: £12.00
- Provides over 4000 French legal words and phrases associated with legislation falling within the Civil Code and the Penal Code, (eg house purchase and wills), but company and commercial legislation is not covered.

HADLEY'S CONVERSATIONAL FRENCH PHRASE BOOK

Paperback, 1997, 256 pages, 148 x 105 mm
ISBN 1-872739-05-9   Price: £6.00
- Over 2000 French/English phrases and 2000 English/French phrases
- Eleven conversational topic vocabularies
- Aide-memoire key word dictionary

GLOSSARY OF MEDICAL, HEALTH AND PHARMACY TERMS

Paperback, 2003, 204 pages, 210 x 148 mm
ISBN 1-872739-12-1   Price: £12.50
- An up-to-date source of over 3000 medical, health and pharmacy terms in French and English covering a wide range of common illnesses and diseases, anatomical terms, first-aid and hospital terms, as well as pharmacy terms embracing medicines, toiletries, cosmetics, health and pharmaceutical products
- Brief aide-memoire definitions of numerous medical terms and useful medical phrases

HADLEY'S FRENCH MOTORING PHRASE BOOK & DICTIONARY

Paperback, 2001, 176 pages, 148 x 105 mm
ISBN 1-872739-09-1   Price: £6.00
- Asking the Way, Road Signs, Car Hire, Parking, Breakdowns, Accidents, Types of Vehicle, Cycling and Motor Sports. Extensive Dictionary
- Over 3000 words and phrases included

CONCISE DICTIONARY OF HOUSE BUILDING (Arranged by Trades)

Paperback, 2001, Second Edition, 256 pages, 210 x 144 mm
ISBN 1-872739-11-3   Price £27.00
- Dictionary is divided into 14 Sections covering various stages and trades employed in house building
- Over 10,000 terms in each language

The above publications are available through good booksellers or can be obtained directly from Hadley Pager Info by sending a cheque to cover the price (postage is free within the UK, add 10% if outside the UK) to **Hadley Pager Info, PO Box 249, Leatherhead, KT23 3WX, England**. Latest Publication List available on request.